Houghton Mifflin

California Math

Daily Routines and Practice

Student Book

- **Daily Routines**
- **Practice**
- **Looking Ahead Activities**

GRADE 4

Visit **Education Place®**
www.eduplace.com/kids

HOUGHTON MIFFLIN BOSTON

Printed in the U.S.A.

ISBN 10: 0-618-96002-3
ISBN 13: 978-0-618-96002-6

   17 18 19 20 21 0868 16 15 14 13
4500417612

Hands On: How Big Is 1 Million?

Problem of the Day ——————————————————— 3 NS 1.2

José scored 8,369 points playing Zap 'Em. Linda scored 8,381 points playing the same game. Who scored the most points?

Number Sense ——————————————————— Gr3 KEY NS 3.2

Find each sum or difference.

1. $\frac{1}{5} + \frac{3}{5}$

2. $\frac{4}{9} + \frac{3}{9}$

3. $\frac{6}{7} - \frac{3}{7}$

4. $\frac{9}{10} - \frac{6}{10}$

Number of the Day ——————————————————— Gr3 NS 2.0

8

How can 8 be written as the answer to an addition, subtraction, multiplication and division problem?

_____

_____

_____

Facts Practice ——————————————————— NS 1.4

Round to the nearest ten.

1. 82

2. 45

3. 376

4. 817

5. 2,584

6. 6,437

Name _____ Date _____

Hands On: How Big Is 1 Million?

CA Standard
KEY NS 1.1

A large container holds 1,000 paper clips. An office-supply store has 1,000 containers of paper clips in stock. Complete the table to show how many paper clips the store has in stock.

	Number of Paper Clip Containers	Number of Paper Clips per Container	Total Number of Paper Clips in Stock
1.	1	1,000	
2.	10		
3.	50		
4.	100		
5.	1,000		

6. How many paper clips does the store have in stock?

_____

✔ Test Practice

Circle the letter of the correct answer.

7. Which number shows one half of 1 million?

   A 50,000   **C** 500,000

   B 5,000   **D** 5,000,000

8. Which number shows one tenth of 1 million?

   A 100   **C** 10,000

   B 1,000   **D** 100,000

Writing Math Would you use hundreds, thousands, or millions to count the number of miles from the earth to the sun? Explain your reasoning.

Place Value Through Hundred Thousands

Problem of the Day ———————————————————— MR 1.1

Approximately how long would it take you to put together a 50-piece jigsaw puzzle: 30 minutes or 3,000 minutes?

Number Sense ————————————————————————— 3NS 1.1

Use Workmat 2 to write each number.

1. four thousand, six

2. twenty-six thousand, nine hundred thirteen

3. seventy-nine thousand, five hundred

4. one hundred thirty-three thousand, eight hundred four

Number of the Day ———————————————————————— NS 4.1

200

What are some ways to show 200?

_____

_____

_____

Facts Practice ——————————————————————— Gr3 KEY NS 2.2

1. 66 − 12   **2.** 54 − 23   **3.** 102 − 18

4. 70 − 48   **5.** 91 − 75   **6.** 46 − 41

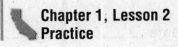
Place Value Through Hundred Thousands

CA Standard
NS 1.0

Write the number in word form.

1. 230,451 _____

_____

2. 137 thousand, 215 _____

_____

Write the number in standard form.

3. six hundred thirteen thousand, five hundred twenty-one _____

4. five thousand, two hundred sixty-seven _____

Write the value of the underlined digit.

5. 5<u>2</u>8   6. <u>7</u>,854   7. 2<u>3</u>6,064   8. 32,8<u>8</u>8

_____   _____   _____   _____

Test Practice

Circle the letter of the correct answer.

9. What form is used to write the number in the statement below?
   About 135,000 people live in my hometown.

   A standard   **C** digit

   B period   **D** word

10. Which of the following shows the number six thousand, seven hundred twenty?

    A 6,720   **C** 60,270

    B 6,270   **D** 67,200

Writing Math What is the value of the digit 5 in 356,017?
Explain how you found your answer.

_____

Place Value Through Hundred Millions

Problem of the Day

KEY NS 1.1

810,870 is written in which number form?

Number Sense Review

KEY NS 1.1

Use Workmat 2 to write the number *seven hundred forty-three* in standard form.

Word of the Day

KEY NS 1.1

place value

How can place value help you tell the number of thousands in 73,060?

_____

_____

_____

Facts Practice

Gr3 KEY NS 2.2

Multiply to find the product.

1. 10 × 5   2. 9 × 8   3. 3 × 7

4. 8 × 4   5. 5 × 5   6. 7 × 6

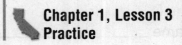
Place Value Through Hundred Millions

CA Standard
KEY NS 1.1

Write the number in word form.

1. 230,451,000 _____

_____

2. 715,413,068 _____

_____

Write the number in standard form.

3. four hundred sixty-three million, three hundred forty-two thousand, seven hundred

   five _____

4. one hundred eighty-five million, three hundred twenty-eight thousand

   _____

Write the value of the 2 in each number.

5. 21,547   6. 54,285   7. 67,902

_____   _____   _____

Test Practice

Circle the letter of the correct answer.

8. Tell what form of the number is being used in the statement below.
   Over 10,000,000 tacos were sold.

   A standard   **B** period   **C** digit   **D** word

9. Which of the following shows the number four hundred eleven million, seven hundred
   twenty-five thousand, six?

   A 4,117,256   **B** 411,725,006   **C** 401,725,060   **D** 4,011,725,006

 Writing Math Write the value of the 4 in 648,396,178.
Explain how you found your answer.

_____

Expanded Notation

Problem of the Day ——————————————— KEY

Cheryl read that the average distance between the sun and the planet
Mars is 141,620,000. What is the value of the digit 4 in this number?
How can this number be written in word form?

Measurement and Geometry ————————————— Gr3 MG 2.4

At the top of your whiteboard draw a right angle. Below the right
angle draw an angle less than a right angle. At the bottom of your
white board draw an angle greater than a right angle.

Word of the Day ———————————————————— KEY

digit

Explain how an infinite number of numbers can be created using just
the digits 0, 1, 2, 3, 4, 5, 6, 7, 8, and 9.

_____

_____

_____

Facts Practice ———————————————————— KEY NS 1.1

Write the value of the underlined digit.

1. 6,0<u>8</u>3,394

2. <u>2</u>,848,389

3. 15,<u>9</u>28,431

4. 7<u>4</u>,592,482

5. 1<u>9</u>4,682,581

6. <u>6</u>53,891,572

Expanded Notation

Write the number in expanded notation.

1. 476,024 _____

2. 81,006,435 _____

_____

Write the number in standard form.

3. 4,000,000 + 200,000 + 80,000 + 800 + 70 + 5 _____

4. 200,000,000 + 2,000,000 + 10,000 + 1,000 + 9 _____

 **Test Practice**

5. Which of the following numbers written in standard form is the correct way to write six hundred forty-seven million, fifty-three thousand, nineteen?

   A 6,475,319   **C** 647,053,019

   B 64,753,019   **D** 6,470,053,019

Circle the letter of the correct answer.

6. Which of the following numbers written in expanded notation is the correct way to write 203,001,510?

   A two million three, one thousand, five hundred ten

   B twenty-three million, one thousand, five hundred ten

   C two hundred three million, one hundred five thousand, ten

   D two hundred three million, one thousand, five hundred ten

 Writing Math Which digits in problem 6 have the same value? Explain.

_____

_____

_____

Problem Solving: Field Trip

Problem of the Day ——————————————————— KEY NS 1.1

On his birthday, Ricardo calculated that he was 5,256,000 minutes old. How can this number be written in expanded form?

Algebra and Functions ——————————————————— Gr 3 AF 2.2

Write the next number in each pattern below.

1. 4, 8, 12, 16 . . .

2. 6, 9, 12, 15 . . .

3. 11, 18, 25, 32 . . .

4. 20, 18, 16, 14 . . .

Number of the Day ——————————————————— KEY NS 1.1

0

Write three numbers in the millions which have no hundred thousands.

_____

_____

_____

Facts Practice ——————————————————— KEY NS 1.1

Write each number in expanded form.

1. 58,298

2. 79,092

3. 303,471

4. 4,371,090

5. 50,042,901

6. 785,391,087

Hands On: Compare and Order Whole Numbers

Problem of the Day —————————————————— KEY NS 1.1

Marco incorrectly wrote the number 1,783,445 in expanded form. He wrote 1,000,000 + 700,000 + 80,000 + 30,000 + 400 + 40 + 5. What did Marco do wrong? Fix his work.

Number Sense —————————————————— KEY NS 1.1

Use Workmat 2 to help write the numbers in word form.

1. 15,781,309

2. 7,829,419

Word of the Day —————————————————— KEY NS 1.2

whole numbers

What does it mean if you eat a *whole* apple? List different ways to show a piece of a number.

_____

_____

_____

Facts Practice —————————————————— KEY NS 1.1

Write the number in the hundreds place for each number.

1. 5,700

2. 8,000

3. 42,000

4. 7,100

5. 3,500

6. 30,900

Daily Routines

11

Use with Chapter 2, Lesson 1

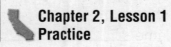
Hands On: Compare and Order Whole Numbers

CA Standard
KEY NS 1.2

Use > or < to compare the numbers. Make a number line on a separate sheet of paper to help.

1. 4,351 ◯ 4,315

2. 60,060 ◯ 6,600

3. 69,780 ◯ 96,870

4. 119,832 ◯ 911,238

5. 745,271 ◯ 75,271

6. 598,401 ◯ 589,410

7. 9,889 ◯ 8,998

8. 30,298 ◯ 30,302

9. 14,501 ◯ 13,799

Test Practice

Circle the letter of the correct answer.

10. A company tracked their quarterly sales. The company sold 7,348 units in March, 8,382 units in June, 6,943 units in September, and 9,348 units in December. During which month did the company sell the least?

A March   **C** June

B September   **D** December

11. There were 9,435 visitors to a park on Sunday, 4,688 on Monday, 9,643 on Wednesday, and 10,092 on Saturday. On which day did the most people visit?

A Sunday   **C** Wednesday

B Monday   **D** Saturday

Writing Math When ordering numbers, is it safe to decide that the number with the most 9s in it is the greatest? Explain.

_____

_____

_____

_____

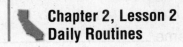
Compare and Order Whole Numbers Through Millions

Problem of the Day ———————————————— KEY NS 1.1

Write 39,914 in expanded notation.

Number Sense ——————————————————— KEY NS 1.2

Use Workmat 4 to find which is greater: 2,471 or 2,476.

Word of the Day ——————————————————— KEY NS 1.1

period

Name the digits in the thousands period of the number 1,454,683.

_____

_____

_____

Facts Practice ————————————————————— Gr3 KEY NS 2.3

Multiply or divide.

1. 28 ÷ 4   **2.** 4 × 6   **3.** 8 × 8

4. 54 ÷ 9   **5.** 9 × 7

Compare and Order Whole Numbers Through Millions

CA Standards
KEY NS 1.2

Compare. Write > or < for each ◯.

1. 718 ◯ 817

2. 7,439 ◯ 77,439

3. 341,762 ◯ 341,672

4. 78,487,231 ◯ 78,482,731

5. 323,332,223 ◯ 323,332,233

6. 73,773,737 ◯ 73,737,737

7. 99,011,032 ◯ 99,010,033

8. 617,860,446 ◯ 617,806,448

Test Practice

9. Jerry took 10,233 steps in one day. Anne took more steps than Jerry. Which amount could be the number of steps Anne took?

   A 10,134   **C** 10,322

   B 9,999   **D** 1,233

10. All of the following numbers are greater than 1,698,477 except which number?

    A 1,700,000   **C** 6,984,777

    B 1,698,488   **D** 1,698,467

Writing Math Jessica is comparing the numbers 5,553,402 and 5,554,937. She thinks she can tell which one is greater by looking in the hundred thousands place. Is she correct? Explain.

_____

_____

_____

_____

_____

_____

Round Whole Numbers

Problem of the Day ——————————————————— MR 2.3

John shows 45, 60, 75, and 80 on a number line.
By how much should each tic mark on the number line increase?

Number Sense ———————————————————————— KEY

Write the value of the underlined digit.

1. 4̲49,206,007

2. 60,8̲01,993

3. 47̲,689

Word of the Day ———————————————————————— KEY

expanded notation

What does expanded notation mean?

_____

_____

_____

Facts Practice ———————————————————————— KEY

Order the numbers from least to greatest.

1. 33; 216; 106; 45

2. 1,015; 1,006; 1,218; 1,296

3. 4,399; 4,407; 4,302; 4,286

4. 5,600; 5,031; 5,301; 5,006

Round Whole Numbers

CA Standard
KEY NS 1.3

Use the number line to round each number to the nearest thousand.

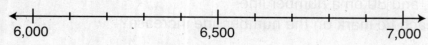

```
  6,000              6,500              7,000
```

1. 6,700   **2.** 6,287   **3.** 6,981   **4.** 6,492

_____   _____   _____   _____

Round each number to the place of the underlined digit.

5. 54,873   **6.** 78,365   **7.** 195,035   **8.** 287,498

_____   _____   _____   _____

 **Test Practice**

Circle the letter of the correct answer.

9. The cash register at a restaurant showed $782.65 in sales for Friday. Round that amount to the nearest ten dollars.

   A $790.00   **c** $780.65

   B $780.70   **D** $780.00

10 The owner of an olive grove rounds the number of olives he harvests to the nearest thousand. If he harvested 12,621 olives, what would be his rounded total?

   A 12,000   **c** 1,200

   B 10,000   **D** 13,000

Writing Math Is it true that if two numbers both round to 1,000 as their nearest thousand, the greatest possible difference between them is 499?

_____

_____

_____

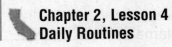

Name _____ Date _____

More on Rounding Whole Numbers

Problem of the Day
KEY NS 1.3

The Sand Hill Elementary school collected 3,478 cans of food during a month long food drive. To the nearest thousand, about how many cans did they collect?

Number Sense

Write the numbers in order from greatest to least.

52,091   52,910   52,109

Number of the Day

72,582

How can this number be changed so when rounded to the nearest thousand it would round to 72,000?

_____

_____

_____

Facts Practice

Compare. Write > or < for each ⬭.

1. 708 ⬭ 809   2. 5,271 ⬭ 5,638   3. 1,873 ⬭ 1,863

4. 17,339 ⬭ 17,551   5. 21,508 ⬭ 20,508   6. 16,881 ⬭ 16,880

More on Rounding Whole Numbers

CA Standard
KEY NS 1.3

Round each number to the place of the underlined digit.

1. 1,38<u>4</u>,792

2. 2,4<u>3</u>2,987

3. 200,<u>9</u>88,083

_____

_____

_____

4. <u>8</u>,489,348

5. 902,<u>7</u>84,893

6. <u>3</u>80,048,345

_____

_____

_____

7. 39,5<u>7</u>1,660

8. <u>9</u>2,482,086

9. 7<u>5</u>,099,600

_____

_____

_____

Circle the letter of the correct answer.

10. The highest mountain in Death Valley National Park is 132,588 inches tall. About how tall is it, rounded to the nearest hundred?

    A 133,000

    c 132,600

    B 600

    D 100,000

11. What is 9,546,004 rounded to the nearest million?

    A 10,000,000

    c 9,000,000

    B 900,000

    D 600,000

Writing Math Thomas is rounding 98,453,087 to the nearest million. Does he need to look at the 0 in the hundreds place? Explain.

_____

_____

_____

_____

Problem Solving: Make an Organized List

Problem of the Day ——————————————————— KEY NS 1.3

A print shop receives two big projects in one day. The first project needs 43,875 copies. The second project needs 28,440 copies. Round the number of copies for each project to the nearest ten thousand.

Number Sense ——————————————————— KEY NS 1.2

Write the numbers in order from least to greatest.

17,998   19,998   17,398

Word of the Day —————————————————————— KEY AF 1.2

digit

What are the digits in the number 685? What is the value of the 6 in 685? What is the value of 8 in 685? What is the value of 5 in 685?

_____

_____

_____

Facts Practice ——————————————————— KEY NS 1.3

Round to the underlined digit.

1. 14,<u>7</u>63

2. 3<u>1</u>,776

3. 153,8<u>7</u>2

4. <u>1</u>87,221

5. 1<u>9</u>0,781

6. 3,<u>8</u>97,408

Problem Solving: Make an Organized List

Problems 21–23
Complete the table and use the information to answer.

The Hillsboro Elementary School had a bake sale to raise money for their class picnic. They sold 76 fruit roll-ups, 135 granola bars, 107 carrot muffins, and 85 slices of banana bread. The students earned $81.00 for the granola bars, $34.00 for the banana bread, $75.00 for the muffins, and $22.80 for the fruit roll-ups.

Item	Number Sold	Number Sold Rounded to Nearest Tenth	Money Earned	Money Earned Rounded to Highest Place
1.	2.	3.	4.	5.
6.	7.	8.	9.	10.
11.	12.	13.	14.	15.
16.	17.	18.	19.	20.

21. About how many items did the students sell?

_____

22. Put the items in order according to the amounts the students earned from greatest to least.

_____

_____

23. About how much did the students earn at the bake sale?

_____

Hands On: Estimate and Check

Problem of the Day ————————————————————— KEY NS 1.3

In 2005, the city of Los Angeles had a population of about 3,844,829.
What is this number rounded to the nearest million?

Number Sense Review ————————————————————— KEY NS 1.2

Order the numbers 56,374,350; 56,374,530; and 55,374,053 from
least to greatest.

Number of the Day ————————————————————— KEY NS 1.1

1,234,567

What is another way the number 1,234,567 can be written?

_____

_____

_____

Facts Practice ————————————————————— KEY NS 1.3

Round each number to the place of the underlined digit.

1. 5,2<u>5</u>4,338

2. <u>3</u>6,094,594

3. 745,<u>3</u>96

4. 276,<u>1</u>38,558

5. 85,<u>7</u>27

6. <u>6</u>61,487,329

Name _____ Date _____

Hand On: Estimate and Check

CA Standard
KEY NS 3.0

Estimate the sum.

1. $19 + 31 + 16 + 39 =$ _____

2. $24 + 42 + 12 + 54 =$ _____

3. $6 + 62 + 48 + 77 =$ _____

4. $94 + 11 + 28 + 70 =$ _____

5. $152 + 114 + 189 =$ _____

6. $87 + 136 + 207 =$ _____

7. $190 + 157 + 38 =$ _____

8. $273 + 42 + 404 =$ _____

✓ Test Practice

Circle the letter of the correct answer.

9. Which is the best estimate of the sum of $71 + 8 + 26$?

   A 90

   B 100

   C 110

   D 120

10. Which is the best estimate of the sum of $333 + 256 + 212$?

    A 750

    B 770

    C 780

    D 800

Writing Math Explain how you used rounding and place value to determine the best estimate in problem 10.

_____

_____

_____

_____

Addition Properties

Problem of the Day ———————————— NS 2.1

Three friends are looking at their collections of toy cars. John has 43
cars, Misha has 28 cars, and Bart has 16 cars. Estimate how many toy
cars the friends have all together.

Number Sense Review ———————————— KEY NS 1.3

Round each number to the nearest million.

1. 1,867,234

2. 340,511,094

3. 76,209,984

Word of the Day ———————————— MR 2.3

compare

What are some examples of when you might need to *compare*
numbers?

_____

_____

Facts Practice ———————————— KEY NS 1.1

Write each number in expanded notation.

1. 4,527,163   2. 60,203,110

3. 821,040,307   4. 9,000,085

Name _____ Date _____

Addition Properties

Find the number that makes each number sentence true.
Tell which property of addition you used.

1. $27 + 45 =$ _____ $+ 27$

_____

_____

2. $(8 + 2) + 38 = 8 +$ _____

_____

_____

3. $782 + 0 =$ _____

_____

_____

4. $(14 + 7) + 6 = 14 +$ _____

_____

_____

Group the addends so you can add mentally.

5. $87 + 42 + 13$

_____

6. $74 + 65 + 26$

_____

7. $260 + 40 + 127$

_____

8. $189 + 123 + 11$

_____

Test Practice

Circle the letter of the correct answer.

9. Brianna picked apples at Shelburne Orchards. She picked 17 Macintosh apples, 49 golden delicious apples, and 83 red delicious apples. How can she group the addends to make it easier to find how many apples she picked altogether?

A $17 + 49 + 83$

B $17 + (83 + 49)$

C $(17 + 83) + 49$

D $(49 + 83) + 17$

10. Ferdinand collected pennies from around his bedroom. He found 2 in a desk drawer, 12 on his dresser, and 98 in his bank. How can he group the addends to make it easier to find how many coins he found altogether?

A $(2 + 12) + 98$

B $(2 + 98) + 12$

C $(98 + 12) + 2$

D $(12 + 2) + 98$

Writing Math Josephine had 86 baseball cards. George gave her 37 more. If David gives Josephine 14 more cards, how many will she have in all? Explain how you found your answer.

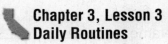
Estimate Sums

Problem of the Day ———————————————————— KEY NS 1.3

Round 473,853 to the nearest ten-thousand.

Number Sense ———————————————————————— KEY NS 1.1

Use Workmat 2 to write each number.

1. three thousand, two hundred two

2. nineteen thousand, nine hundred

3. sixty-five thousand

4. four hundred seven thousand, eight hundred thirteen

Word of the Day ———————————————————————— AF 1.0

Zero Property of Addition

Use your white board to write an addition sentence using the Zero
Property of Addition.

_____

_____

Facts Practice ——————————————————————— KEY NS 1.1

Write each number in Standard form.

1. 1,000 + 10 + 7   **2.** 10,000 + 6

3. 40,000 + 7,000 + 300 + 8   **4.** 100,000 + 90,000 + 9,000 + 500 + 40 + 1

Estimate Sums

CA Standards
KEY NS 1.3, KEY NS 3.0

Round each number to the nearest ten. Then estimate the sum.

1. $246 + 148 =$
_____

2. $\begin{array}{r} 851 \\ + 189 \\ \hline \end{array}$

3. $\begin{array}{r} 7,412 \\ + 7,627 \\ \hline \end{array}$

4. $472 + 368 =$
_____

Round each number to the nearest hundred. Then estimate the sum.

5. $373 + 227 =$
_____

6. $\begin{array}{r} 5,355 \\ + 2,798 \\ \hline \end{array}$

Round each number to the greatest place. Then estimate the sum.

7. $3,458 + 2,683 =$
_____

8. $\begin{array}{r} 2,648 \\ + 5,712 \\ \hline \end{array}$

Test Practice

Circle the letter of the correct answer.

9. Last month Timothy read two books. The first book was 187 pages long, and the second book was 268 pages long. If you round each number to the nearest ten, which of the following is the best estimate of the number of pages he read in all?

   A 400   **B** 440   **C** 460   **D** 500

10. The Robert H. Meyer Memorial State Beach covers about 37 acres. The Will Rogers State Beach is about 82 acres. If you round each number to the nearest ten, which of the following is the best estimate of the total number of acres these two beaches cover?

   A 110   **B** 120   **C** 130   **D** 150

Writing Math In Problem 10, suppose you had rounded to the nearest hundred. Would that give a better estimate of the sum? Explain your answer.

_____

_____

_____

Add Whole Numbers

Problem of the Day ———————————————————— NS 2.1

Sara will win a new bike if she sells over 2,500 rolls of wrapping paper in a fundraiser. Last month she sold 1,116 rolls, and this month she sold 1,378 rolls. Has Sara sold enough wrapping paper to win the bike?

Number Sense Review ———————————————— KEY NS 1.1

Write the number seven hundred two million, thirty-six thousand, four hundred fifty-eight in standard form.

Word of the Day ———————————————————————— MR 2.3

round

What are some different situations in which you might need to *round*?

_____

_____

_____

Facts Practice —————————————————————————— AF 1.0

Identify the property of addition.

1. $5 + 7 = 7 + 5$

2. $18 + 0 = 18$

3. $(12 + 3) + 5 = 12 + (3 + 5)$

4. $0 + 66 = 66$

Add Whole Numbers

CA Standards
KEY NS 3.1, KEY NS 3.0

Add. Use estimation to verify your answer.

1. 184
    +714

2. 632
    + 89

3. 2,485
    +2,467

4. 3,894
    +6,113

5. $387 + 692 + 245 =$

6. $5,481 + 2,374 + 1,954 =$

7. $3,482 + 5,423 + 8,234 =$

8. $26,569 + 43,047 =$ _____

9. $58,715 + 94,528 =$ _____

Test Practice

Circle the letter of the correct answer.

10. In the most recent census, the city of Benicia had a population of 26,865. On the same census, the city of Berkeley had a population of 102,743. At the time of the census, how many people lived in these two cities?

    A 128,508   C 128,608

    B 129,508   D 129,608

11. Byron finished 237 math problems. Jessica finished 382 math problems. Grace finished 493 math problems. How many math problems were finished?

    A 112   C 1,212

    B 1,121   D 1,112

Writing Math David spent $29.45 on books, $38.67 on groceries, and $18.54 on gasoline for his car. How much did David spend altogether? Explain how you found your answer.

_____

Problem Solving: Field Trip

Problem of the Day ——————————————— KEY NS 3.1

Ken ran 75 miles in February to begin preparing for a marathon. He ran 106 miles in March, and 120 miles in April. How many miles has he run all together?

Number Sense Review ——————————————— KEY NS 1.4

Use Workmat 1 to write down whether you need an estimate or an exact amount to solve the problem.

A summer camp has space for 650 children to attend. They have 326 applications from boys, and 308 applications from girls. Can all the applications be accepted?

Number of the Day ——————————————— NS 2.1

21

What numbers can be added to 21 that would require regrouping in the ones place?

_____

_____

_____

Facts Practice ——————————————— KEY NS 1.2

Compare. Fill in the blank with >, <, or =.

1. 68,450,021 ____ 68,420,021

2. 32,871,203 ____ 9,204,304

3. 98,394,797 ____ 111,394,013

4. 5,687,321 ____ 5,687,321

5. 202,002,002 ____ 222,220,002

6. 410,098,451 ____ 414,098,451

Hands On: Model Subtraction from 2,000

Problem of the Day ———————————————— MR 2.3

The table below shows the number of visitors to a zoo over one week.

Day	Number of Visitors
Weekdays	5,182
Saturday	3,891
Sunday	3,036

Looking at the table, how would you find about how many people attended the zoo in one week?

Number Sense ———————————————— KEY NS 1.2

On your whiteboard, write three different numbers which are less than nine hundred fifty thousand, but greater than nine hundred forty-nine thousand.

Number of the Day ———————————————— KEY NS 1.3

300

Write two numbers greater than 300 and two numbers less than 300 which would round to 300.

_____

_____

Facts Practice ———————————————— KEY NS 3.1

Find each sum.

1. 152 + 343

2. 783 + 854

3. 54,198 + 2,003

4. 16,592 + 405,213

5. 129 + 452 + 1,490

6. 5,391 + 2,310 + 4,007

Daily Routines

31

Use with Chapter 4, Lesson 1

Name _____ Date _____

Hands On: Model Subtraction from 2,000

CA Standard
KEY NS 3.1

Subtract. Use play money to help.

1. $2,000 − $691 =

_____

2. $2,000 − $821 =

_____

3. $2,000 − $437 =

_____

4. $2,000 − $585 =

_____

5. $2,000 − $200 =

_____

6. $2,000 − $372 =

_____

Subtract using regrouping.

7. 2,000 − 936 =

_____

8. 2,000 − 21 =

_____

9. 2,000 − 704 =

_____

10. 2,000 − 199 =

_____

11. 2,000 − 543 =

_____

12. 2,000 − 881 =

_____

Test Practice

Circle the letter of the correct answer.

13. How much is $309 subtracted from $2,000?

   A $1,609

   B $1,691

   C $1,702

   D $1,093

14. In the problem 2,000 − 642, which places have to be regrouped?

   A tens, hundreds, thousands

   B tens, thousands

   C hundreds, thousands

   D ones, tens, hundreds

Writing Math Dale did the problem 2,000 − 850 and got the answer 2,150. What did he do wrong to get this answer? Explain.

_____

_____

Estimate Differences

Problem of the Day

Anna has 312 photos in her scrapbook; 120 photos are of family members. How many photos in the scrapbook are not of family members?

Number Sense

Label each point on the number line.

10, 60, 110

0 20 40 60 80 100 120 140

Word of the Day

sum

When adding, will you find the sum or the difference?

_____

_____

_____

Facts Practice

Compare using >, <, or =.

1. 4,152 ⬭ 4,512

2. 6,001 ⬭ 10,000

3. 433,001 ⬭ 334,001

4. 615,555 ⬭ 615,555

5. 99,999 ⬭ 999,999

6. 800,000 ⬭ 777,777

Estimate Differences

CA Standards
KEY NS 1.3, NS 2.1

Round each number to the nearest hundred. Then estimate the difference.

1. $6,324 - 4,213 =$

_____

2. $22,937 - 14,679 =$

_____

3. $57,627 - 12,309 =$

_____

4. $4,583 - 2,777 =$

_____

5. $85,533 - 32,486 =$

_____

6. $8,792 - 3,934 =$

_____

Round each number to the nearest thousand. Then estimate the difference.

7. $5,355 - 2,798 =$

_____

8. $68,709 - 40,999 =$

_____

9. $7,063 - 2,395 =$

_____

 **Test Practice**

Circle the letter of the correct answer.

10. The Larson family drove 10,820 miles in their van. They drove 7,296 miles in their compact car. About how many more miles did they drive with the van? Round each number to the nearest hundred and estimate.

   A 1,500 miles   **C** 3,500 miles

   B 2,500 miles   **D** 4,000 miles

11. Crystal's home town has 62,784 people. Simon's home town has 87,200 people. About how many more people live in Simon's town than Crystal's town? Round each number to the nearest thousand and estimate.

   A 24,000   **C** 35,000

   B 30,000   **D** 15,000

Writing Math The teacher asked Lewis and Kara to round the number 62,500 to the nearest thousand. Lewis's answer was 63,000 and Kara's was 62,000. Are they both right? Explain.

_____

_____

Name _____ Date _____

Subtract Whole Numbers

Problem of the Day ———————————————— KEY

Emma has 678 pennies. Her sister has 452 pennies. How many
pennies will they have if they combine their money?

Number Sense ———————————————————— KEY NS 1.2

Order the following numbers from greatest to least.

151,430; 157,888; 160,000; 149,999

Number of the Day ————————————————————— MR 2.3

24

Describe two ways you can use the number 24 today.

_____

_____

_____

Facts Practice ———————————————————— KEY

Add to find the sum.

1. 6,433 + 1,999   **2.** 10,627 + 4,389   **3.** 11,111 + 998

4. 42,189 + 715   **5.** 52,061 + 6,081   **6.** 108,327 + 456,113

Name _____ Date _____

Subtract Whole Numbers

CA Standards
KEY NS 3.1, **KEY** NS 3.0

Subtract. Use addition to check.

1. $\begin{array}{r} 924 \\ -735 \\ \hline \end{array}$

2. $\begin{array}{r} 672 \\ -49 \\ \hline \end{array}$

3. $\begin{array}{r} 3,245 \\ -860 \\ \hline \end{array}$

4. $\begin{array}{r} 849 \\ -364 \\ \hline \end{array}$

5. $\begin{array}{r} 6,492 \\ -881 \\ \hline \end{array}$

6. $7,402 - 4,829 =$

_____

7. $9,266 - 4,157 =$

_____

8. $5,481 - 1,954 =$

_____

9. $6,648 - 5,471 =$

_____

10. $6,981 - 6,549 =$

_____

11. $8,482 - 3,234 =$

_____

Find each missing number.

12. $29 + \blacksquare = 86$

_____

13. $\blacksquare - 64 = 802$

_____

14. $\blacksquare + 364 = 863$

_____

15. $\blacksquare - 292 = 605$

_____

16. $904 + \blacksquare = 999$

_____

17. $\blacksquare + 284 = 438$

_____

Test Practice

Circle the correct answer.

18. Ura bicycled 2,489 miles in 2003. In 2004, she bicycled 2,892 miles. How many more miles did she bicycle in 2004 than in 2003?

   A 400   **C** 304

   B 403   **D** 300

19. A concert hall seats 2,342 people. If 1,973 people attended last night's concert, how many seats were unoccupied?

   A 300 seats   **C** 369 seats

   B 469 seats   **D** 339 seats

Writing Math Gregory and Millie each raised $370 for their class trip. If $3,560 was raised by the entire class, how much was raised by the rest of the students? Explain how you found your answer.

_____

Subtract Across Zeros

Problem of the Day ————————————————— KEY NS 3.1

Mrs. Chen wants to buy a new computer. Computer Barn sells one for $1,134. PC Hut sells a similar computer for $987. How much would Mrs. Chen save by buying from PC Hut?

Number Sense ——————————————————————— AF 1.0

Write three number sentences on your whiteboard. Make the first sentence show the Associative Property of Addition, make the second show the Commutative Property of Addition, and make the third show the Zero Property of Addition.

Word of the Day ———————————————————————— MR 2.3

difference

Give some real examples of when you might need to find the difference between two numbers.

_____

_____

_____

Facts Practice ———————————————————————————— NS 2.1

Round each addend to the nearest hundred and estimate the sum.

1. $654 + 241$

2. $894 + 342$

3. $4,391 + 2,007$

4. $995 + 2,332$

5. $2,642 + 5,014$

6. $527 + 7,632$

Name _____ Date _____

Subtract Across Zeros

CA Standards
KEY NS 3.1, KEY NS 3.0

Subtract. Estimate or add to check.

1. 408
−254

2. 680
−385

3. 902
−888

4. 300
−148

5. 2,051
−762

6. 4,005 − 846 =

7. 5,602
−947

8. 7,020
−963

9. $30.09
−23.52

10. $90.00
−54.13

11. 8,012 − 1,609 =

12. $90.05
−45.07

13. 5,500 − 2,801 =

14. 7,209 − 4,222 =

15. 6,008
−5489

16. 7,080 − 5,093 =

17. $40.09 − $22.44 =

18. $80.00 − 67.33 =

Test Practice

Circle the correct answer.

19. Leah plans to write 200 pages for her book by the end of the year. So far, she has written 124 pages. How many more pages must she write to meet her goal?

A 200　　C 124

B 176　　D 76

20. A folksinger made 1,000 copies of his current CD. So far, he has sold 583 copies. How many copies does he have left?

A 417　　C 317

B 400　　D 471

Writing Math Oren plans to drive 3,200 miles from the East Coast to the West Coast. So far, he has driven 1,789 miles. How many miles are left to drive? Explain how you found your answer.

_____

_____

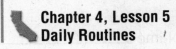
Problem Solving: Too Much or Too Little Information

Problem of the Day ————————————————— KEY NS 3.1

Jamal's youngest sister was born in 2004. Jamal was born in 1986. How many years older than his youngest sister is Jamal?

Number Sense ————————————————— MR 2.3

Make an organized list to find how many numbers between 1,500 and 1,700 have a 0 in the ones place and round to 1,600.

Number of the Day ————————————————— KEY NS 3.1

245

Write two subtraction problems with a difference of 245. One problem should involve regrouping tens as ones, and one should involve regrouping hundreds as tens.

_____

_____

_____

Facts Practice ————————————————— KEY NS 3.1

Find each difference.

1. 487 − 315

2. 958 − 587

3. 2,752 − 1,429

4. 4,401 − 2,803

5. 38,491 − 22,593

6. 59,825 − 36,758

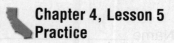
Problem Solving:
Too Much or Too Little Information

CA Standards
MR 1.1, KEY NS 3.1

Mrs. Winter is planning a party for her class.

Use the information on the table to answer problems 1–3. If not enough information is given, tell what information is needed to solve the problem.

Item	Number of Servings
Cranberry Juice	8 per gallon
Pretzels	10 per bag
Apple Slices	2 per apple
Almonds	4 per bag
String Cheese Sticks	24 per bag

1. Mrs. Winter has 24 students. If she sets aside $10 for juice, will the students have enough to drink?

_____

_____

2. Mrs. Winter bought 3 bags of pretzels, 1 bag of string cheese sticks, and 6 bags of almonds. How many servings of pretzels will she have left over?

_____

Test Practice

Circle the letter of the correct answer.

3. Henry drank 2 bottles of water on Saturday, 4 bottles on Monday, and 1 bottle on Tuesday. How many more bottles of water did he drink than last week?

   A not enough information

   B too much information

   C 3 more

   D 4 more

4. Nadia finds 3 coins under her bed, 3 times that many under the couch, and $\frac{1}{3}$ as many in her coat pocket. How many coins did she find in all?

   A not enough information

   B too much information

   C 7 coins

   D 13 coins

Writing Math Alexis has been given a problem with too much information. What should she do?

_____

_____

Hands On: Expressions with Parentheses

Problem of the Day ———————————————— KEY NS 3.0

Amanda has soccer practice 60 minutes on Monday, 45 minutes on Wednesday, and 90 minutes on Saturday. On Tuesday she practices the piano 45 minutes. How many minutes does Amanda practice soccer each week? What information was not needed?

Number Sense ———————————————— KEY NS 1.3 NS 3.0

Round to the nearest hundred. Then estimate each sum.

1. 350 + 498

2. 762 + 539

3. 1,832 + 3,439

4. 2,892 + 4,428

Word of the Day ———————————————— MR 2.3

difference

Can you get a difference by adding two numbers?
What is the difference between 5 and 3?

_____

_____

_____

Facts Practice ———————————————— KEY NS 3.1

Subtract.

1. 428 − 275   2. 1,387 − 1,211   3. 7,367 − 4,312

4. 5,129 − 3,287   5. 6,882 − 4,310   6. 9,615 − 3,087

Name _____ Date _____

Hands On: Expressions with Parentheses

Add parentheses to make the value of the expression equal to 10.

1. $12 - 6 + 4$ **2.** $20 - 7 + 3$ **3.** $31 - 22 + 1$

4. $7 - 4 + 7$ **5.** $19 - 5 + 4$ **6.** $14 - 8 + 4$

Use the numbers to make an expression with a value of 42.
Be sure to use +, −, and parentheses in each expression.

7. 73, 40, 9 _____

8. 27, 6, 21 _____

9. 55, 6, 7 _____

Test Practice

Circle the letter of the correct answer.

10. Which expression has a value of 8?

   A $14 - (5 + 1)$ **C** $23 - (7 + 7)$

   B $(9 - 5) + 5$ **D** $(8 - 7) + 9$

11. Which number makes the expression correct?

   $(13 + \square) - 18 = 3$

   A 2   **C** 5

   B 8   **D** 9

Writing Math Why does it *not* matter where you put the parentheses to evaluate $8 + 12 - 10$?

_____

_____

Write and Evaluate Expressions

Problem of the Day

Bert says the answer to the expression $12 - (8 + 3)$ is 7.
Is his answer correct? If not, what did he do wrong?

Number Sense

Choose the greater number.

1. 7,892   7,982

2. 5,329   5,923

3. 16,705   16,057

4. 158,235   152,385

Word of the Day

operation

What are the four major operations in mathematics? How can you
compare the meaning of *operation* in mathematics to the meaning
of *operation* a doctor performs?

_____

_____

_____

Facts Practice

Add.

1. $726 + 159$ 2. $562 + 763$ 3. $1,728 + 1,220$

4. $5,672 + 1,783$ 5. $6,339 + 5,823$ 6. $18,338 + 11,552$

Name _____ Date _____

Write and Evaluate Expressions

CA Standards
KEY AF 1.2, AF 1.0

Write an expression for the situation.

1. 17 fewer than 30 _____

2. 86 more than 5 _____

3. 412 minus the sum of 27 and 8 _____

4. 55 more than the difference between 90 and 33 _____

5. 64 fewer than the sum of 72 and 101 _____

6. 9 more than the sum of 166 and 59 _____

Simplify the expression.

7. $(20 - 9) + 36$ _____

8. $(31 + 18) + (42 - 27)$ _____

9. $100 - (5 + 6 + 7)$ _____

Test Practice

Circle the letter of the correct answer.

10. Simplify the expression.

$(47 - 5) - (29 + 3)$

A 10   **C** 20

B 26   **D** 74

11. Which is an expression for 13 more than the difference between 404 and 305?

A $(404 - 305) - 13$

B $(404 + 305) - 13$

C $(404 - 305) + 13$

D $(404 + 305 + 13)$

 Writing Math Explain how to simplify an expression with parentheses.

_____

_____

Expressions, Equations, and Inequalities

Problem of the Day —————————————————————— KEY NS 1.1

Write one hundred seventy-two million, six hundred two thousand,
nine in expanded notation.

Number Sense —————————————————————— KEY NS 1.2

Compare. Write >, <, or = for each **.**

1. 1,789 ⬭ 1,978

2. 23,887 ⬭ 23,988

3. 4 + 2 ⬭ 8 − 2

4. 17 − 5 ⬭ 3 + 5

Number of the Day —————————————————————— KEY AF 1.2

8

What are a few different numbers sentences that use parentheses that
make 8?

_____

_____

Facts Practice —————————————————————— KEY NS 1.3

Round to the underlined digit.

1. 1$\underline{8}$,332

2. 219,$\underline{6}$50

3. 1$\underline{1}$5,873

4. $\underline{8}$93,443

5. 52,87$\underline{3}$,117

6. 1$\underline{7}$6,329,174

Name _____ Date _____

Expressions, Equations, and Inequalities

CA Standards
KEY AF 1.2, AF 1.0

Write whether the number sentence is an expression, an inequality, or an equation.

1. $(99 - 14) + 5$ _____

2. $8 + (110 - 25) = 565 - 472$ _____

3. $(75 - 4) + 17 > 144 - (49 + 18)$ _____

Complete by using >, <, or =.

4. $(18 - 10) + 3 \bigcirc 18 - (10 + 3)$

5. $9 + (101 - 50) \bigcirc 30 + 30$

6. $49 - (12 + 7) \bigcirc (16 + 18) - 2$

Complete.

7. $17 + 2 = (12 - \square) + 8 \; \boxed{}$

8. $(5 + \square) + (20 - 16) = 7 + 17 \; \boxed{}$

9. $56 + \square = 81 - (5 + 4) \; \boxed{}$

✓ Test Practice

Circle the letter of the correct answer.

10. Which word describes the number sentence?

$(20 - 6) + 5 < 12 + 8$

A equality   C equation

B expression   D inequality

11. Which symbol makes the number sentence true?

$(90 - 73) + 42 \bigcirc 30 + 26$

A +   C >

B <   D =

Writing Math What is an equation?

_____

_____

Add Equals to Equals

Problem of the Day ——————————————————— KEY AF 1.2

What are all of the possible numbers that can fill in the _____ to make the inequality true?

$(18 - 3) + 5 > (12 + \underline{\quad}) - 1$

Algebra and Functions ——————————————————— AF 1.0

Write an expression for each word phrase.

1. the difference of 12 and 2

2. the sum of 5 and 3

3. 212 minus the sum of 18 and 100

4. 12 more than the difference of 18 and 5

Word of the Day ——————————————————— MR 2.3

equation

What is the difference between an equation and an expression?

_____

_____

_____

Facts Practice ——————————————————— KEY NS 1.3

Round each number to the nearest thousand. Then subtract.

1. $3,872 - 1,562$

2. $6,302 - 2,221$

3. $12,673 - 7,581$

4. $10,721 - 3,187$

5. $14,271 - 10,998$

6. $37,729 - 21,582$

Add Equals to Equals

CA Standards
KEY AF 2.0, KEY AF 2.1

Complete.

1. $51 + 48 = 99$

   _____ $= 99$

2. $86 - 37 =$ _____

   _____ $=$ _____

3. _____ $= 105 - 26$

   _____ $=$ _____

4. $(75 - 13) + 21 = 62 + 21$

   _____ $+ 21 =$ _____

   _____ $=$ _____

5. $(88 - 40) + 25 = 48 + 25$

   _____ $+ 25 =$ _____

   _____ $=$ _____

6. $60 + (36 + 11) = 60 + 47$

   $60 +$ _____ $=$ _____

Compare the expressions. Write $\neq$ or $=$ to make each true.

7. $31 + 47 \bigcirc (22 + 5 + 51)$

   $(31 + 47) + 12 \bigcirc (22 + 5 + 51) + 12$

8. $400 - 366 \bigcirc 18 + 5 + 21$

   $59 + (400 - 366) \bigcirc 59 + (18 + 5 + 21)$

Test Practice

Circle the letter of the correct answer.

9. What is the missing number?

   $71 + 18 = \boxed{}$

   A 18   **C** 53

   B 71   **D** 89

10. Which symbol makes the number sentence true?

    $2 + (83 - 6) \bigcirc 2 + (85 - 4)$

    A $=$ **C** $>$

    B $+$ **D** $<$

Writing Math Can the values on both sides of the equals sign be different?

_____

_____

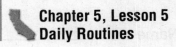

Name _____ Date _____

Problem Solving: Break a Problem into Parts

Problem of the Day ——————————————— KEY AF 2.1

Find the number that makes the equation true.

$(13 + 21) - 16 =$ ____ -16

Number Sense ——————————————————— KEY NS 3.1

Urmi was using play money to subtract $3,782-$1,518.
Explain how she would need to regroup in order to subtract.

Number of the Day ————————————————— KEY NS 3.0

$108

Using play money, what is the least amount of bills that could be used
to represent $108? How do you know?

_____

_____

_____

Facts Practice ——————————————————— KEY NS 3.1

Find the number that makes each number sentence true.
Tell which property of addition you used.

1. $15 + 9 =$ ____ $+ 15$

2. $17 +$ ____ $= 17$

3. $(5 + 19) + 1 = 5 + ($ ____ $+ 1)$

4. $3 + 17 = 17 +$ ____

5. $15 + 2 + 5 = 15 +$ ____ $+ 2$

Name _____ Date _____

Problem Solving: Break a Problem into Parts

CA Standards
MR 1.2, **KEY** AF 1.3

Use the information from the table to write an expression
to solve the problems.

	Sierra Nevada Ranges	Cascade Ranges
Bluebirds	37	32
Downy Woodpeckers	17	11
Chickadees	42	29

1. How many more birds were counted in the Sierra Nevadas than in the Cascades?

_____

2. How many more bluebirds than woodpeckers were counted?

_____

Test Practice

Circle the letter of the correct answer.

3. Renee wants to know how many more woodpeckers and chickadees were counted in the Sierra Nevadas than in the Cascades. What expression should she use?

   A $(17 + 11) - (19 + 15)$ **C** $(17 + 42) - (11 + 29)$

   B $(42 + 55) - (32 - 35)$ **D** $(17 + 19) - (11 + 15)$

4. The birdwatchers in the Sierra Nevadas saw 5 of the woodpeckers in tree cavities. They saw 7 of the bluebirds in tree cavities. Choose the expression that tells how many of the woodpeckers and bluebirds counted in the Sierra Nevadas were not in tree cavities.

   A $(11 - 5) + (15 - 7) = 25$ **C** $(17 - 5) + (37 - 7) = 42$

   B $(5 + 7) + (17 + 19) = 48$ **D** $(17 + 19) + (5 + 7) = 48$

 Writing Math When is it helpful to break a problem into smaller parts?

_____

_____

Hands On: Relate Multiplication and Division

Problem of the Day KEY AF 1.3

Kaleigh saw 11 robins and 8 finches in her backyard yesterday morning. This morning she saw 7 robins and 5 finches.
How many more birds did she see yesterday?

Number Sense Review KEY NS 3.1

In what place would you need to start regrouping if subtracting a number from 340,000?

Number of the Day NS 1.0

9

Nine is the number of place values in one hundred million.
What are the names of those place values?

_____

_____

_____

Facts Practice KEY NS 3.1

Add.

1. 94,204 + 25,489

2. 6,673 + 729

3. 14,056 + 8,422

4. 5,241 + 5,967

5. 31,489 + 42,330

6. 121,854 + 48,326

Name _____ Date _____

Hands On: Relate Multiplication to Division

Write all the multiplication and division equations for each array.

1.

2. ● ● ● ● ● ●
   ● ● ● ● ● ●
   ● ● ● ● ● ●
   ● ● ● ● ● ●

3.

4.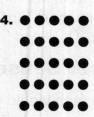

_____ _____ _____ _____

_____ _____ _____ _____

_____ _____ _____ _____

Test Practice

Circle the letter of the correct answer.

5. Which equation does *not* go with the array?

   ● ● ● ●
   ● ● ● ●
   ● ● ● ●

   A $4 \times 3 = 12$ **C** $4 + 3 = 12$

   B $3 \times 4 = 12$ **D** $12 \div 3 = 4$

6. There are 3 rows of 3 counters each. Which equation goes with this array?

   A $3 + 3 = 6$

   B $3 \times 3 = 9$

   C $3 \div 3 = 1$

   D $9 - 3 = 6$

 Writing Math Can you make an array with 23 counters? Explain your answer.

_____

_____

Relate Multiplication and Division

Problem of the Day ————————————— KEY NS 1.1

Write 4,378,619 in expanded notation.

Number Sense ————————————————— KEY NS 1.1

Use Workmat 2 to write seventy-three million, eight hundred
sixteen thousand, four hundred forty-five in standard form.

Word of the Day ————————————————— AF 1.1

equation

Do equations always have an equals sign?

_____

_____

_____

Facts Practice ———————————————— Gr3 KEY NS 2.2

Multiply.

1. 3×7 **2.** 5×6 **3.** 8×8

4. 7×9 **5.** 2×9 **6.** 4×9

Relate Multiplication and Division

CA Standard
KEY NS 3.0

Write the fact family for each array or set of numbers.

1.

2.

3. 2, 7, 14

_____

_____

_____

_____

_____

_____

_____

_____

_____

Complete the fact family.

4. $3 \times 9 = \square$
   $9 \times \square = 27$

   $\square \div 3 = 9$
   $27 \div \square = 3$

5. $5 \times 7 = \square$
   $7 \times \square = 35$

   $\square \div 5 = 7$
   $35 \div \square = 5$

Test Practice

Circle the letter of the correct answer.

6. Find the missing number:

   $\square \times 7 = 63$

   A 6   C 7

   B 8   D 9

7. Find the missing number:

   $48 \div \square = 6$

   A 6   C 7

   B 8   D 9

Writing Math Give an example of a fact family that contains only two "members." Explain why there are two and not four members.

_____

_____

_____

Use with text pp. 122–123

Multiplication Properties and Division Rules

Problem of the Day ——————————————————— KEY NS 3.0

If $7 \times 9 = 63$, what is $63 \div 9$?

Algebra and Functions Review ——————————— KEY AF 1.3

Use Workmat 1 to write down the expression $7 - 2 + 3 - 1$.
Add parentheses so the value of the expression is equal to 1.

Word of the Day ——————————————————————— MR 1.1

inverse operations

What is the *inverse operation* of each of the following expressions?

1. $45 + 16$

2. $56 \div 7$

3. $82 - 39$

4. 15×3

_____

_____

_____

Facts Practice ———————————————————————— KEY NS 3.1

Subtract.

1. $7,452 - 2,626$ **2.** $9,386 - 129$ **3.** $16,924 - 3,945$

4. $48,391 - 39,733$ **5.** $8,193 - 7,642$ **6.** $56,247 - 485$

Daily Routines
55
Use with Chapter 6, Lesson 3

Multiplication Properties and Division Rules

Use properties and rules to solve.

1. $1 \times 436 = \square$

_____

2. $122 \times 17 = 17 \times \square$

_____

3. $(10 \times 85) \times 12 = 10 \times (\square \times 12)$

_____

4. $0 \div 125,699 = \square$

_____

5. $\square \div 1 = 999$

_____

6. $5,133 \times 0 = \square$

_____

7. $848 \div 0 = \square$

_____

8. $\square \div 423 = 1$

_____

Test Practice

Circle the letter of the correct answer.

9. Which is an example of the Identity Property of Multiplication?

A $14 \times 0 = 0$

B $(6 \times 2) \times 8 = 6 \times (2 \times 8)$

C $83 \times 0 = 83$

D $1 \times 555 = 555$

10. Which is true about division sentences that include 0?

A $0 \div 8 = 8$

B $8 \div 0 = 0$

C $0 \div 8 = 0$

D $8 \div 0 = 8$

Writing Math Compare the products of 4×0 and $444,444 \times 0$. Explain.

_____

_____

Hands On: Patterns in Multiplication and Division

Problem of the Day
KEY NS 3.0

An array has 5 rows and 4 counters in each row.
Use the array to write multiplication and division equations.

Number Sense
KEY NS 3.1

A hiker climbs 704 feet and then 235 feet before descending 150 feet. How high is she?

Number of the Day
KEY NS 1.1

10

Give an example of when you might need to multiply by 10.

_____

_____

_____

Facts Practice
KEY NS 3.1

Add or subtract.

1. $156 + 72$

2. $297 + 13 - 100$

3. $837 - 490$

4. $(1,023 - 211) + 15$

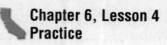
Hands On: Patterns in Multiplication and Division

CA Standard
KEY NS 3.0, MR 2.3

Use a multiplication table to answer each question.

1. List different multiples of 8 that are shown in the table.

   _____

2. Is 42 a square number? Why or why not?

   _____

3. Use the table to find the quotient of 56 ÷ 7. Describe how you found it.

   _____

   _____

4. Find 12 in four different places in the table. Write a division sentence for each 12 you find.

   _____

5. Use the table to find the product of 4 × 7. Describe how you found it.

   _____

   _____

 **Test Practice**

Circle the letter of the correct answer.

6. Which number is a square number?

   A 15   **C** 25

   B 35   **D** 48

7. 15 is the product of which factors?

   A 8 × 7,   **C** 15 × 0,
      7 × 8   0 × 15

   B 5 × 2,   **D** 5 × 3,
      2 × 5   3 × 5

Writing Math What pattern do square numbers form on the multiplication table?

_____

_____

Division with Remainders

Problem of the Day
KEY **NS 3.0**

Write a fact family using the numbers 4, 9, and 36.

Algebra and Functions Review
KEY **AF 2.1**

If $54 + 638 = 54 + (329 + 309)$, can you find the value of the expression in the parentheses without adding?

Number of the Day
AF 1.0

1

What is the difference between adding by 1 and multiplying by 1?

_____

_____

_____

Facts Practice
KEY **AF 1.3**

Simplify each expression.

1. $(22 - 5) + 12$

2. $(30 - 14) + 41$

3. $(93 - 60) + (36 + 8)$

4. $(77 - 52) + (16 - 9)$

5. $100 - (33 + 7) + 4$

6. $84 - (45 + 27) + 8$

Division with Remainders

CA Standard
KEY NS 3.2

Divide.

1. $4\overline{)14}$ 2. $2\overline{)7}$ 3. $3\overline{)20}$ 4. $6\overline{)26}$ 5. $5\overline{)36}$

_____   _____   _____   _____   _____

6. $8\overline{)34}$ 7. $7\overline{)40}$ 8. $9\overline{)17}$ 9. $6\overline{)32}$ 10. $3\overline{)28}$

_____   _____   _____   _____   _____

11. $40 \div 6 =$ 12. $37 \div 7 =$ 13. $80 \div 7 =$ 14. $55 \div 9 =$ 15. $41 \div 7 =$

_____   _____   _____   _____   _____

Find each missing number.

16. $4 \div \square = 1\ R1$ 17. $10 \div 3 = 3\ R\square$ 18. $33 \div 9 = 3\ R\square$

19. $\square \div 7 = 6\ R2$ 20. $\square \div 4 = 7\ R3$ 21. $110 \div \square = 12\ R2$

Test Practice

Circle the letter of the correct answer.

22. Mary is packing plates in boxes. She has 93 plates. Each box holds 8 plates. If she fills each box, how many boxes will she fill, and how many plates will be left over?

    A 11 R3   **C** 11 R5

    B 12 R3   **D** 12 R5

23. Jen has 47 stickers. She wants to give an equal number of stickers to each of her 5 cousins. How many stickers will she give each cousin, and how many stickers will be left over?

    A 6 R5   **C** 7 R5

    B 8 R7   **D** 9 R2

Writing Math Jim solved $6\overline{)39}$ and got the quotient 5 R9. Explain why Jim's answer is incorrect.

_____

_____

Problem Solving: Field Trip

Problem of the Day ——————————————— KEY NS 3.4

Ryan has 44 stickers he wants to give away to 7 friends. If he divides the stickers up equally between his friends, how many stickers will he have left over?

Number Sense Review ——————————————— KEY NS 1.1

What is the value of the digit 6 in each number?

1. 456,703,249

2. 321,762,057

3. 698,343,109

Word of the Day ——————————————— MR 2.3

inequality

What are the different symbols you have learned that show an *inequality?* What is the difference between these symbols?

_____

_____

_____

Facts Practice ——————————————— KEY AF 2.1

Copy and complete.

1. $36 + 29 = 65$
    $= 65$

2. $15 + (64 + 8) = 15 + 72$
   $15 +$ ⬭ $=$ ⬭ $+ 72$

3. $(94 - 58) + 47 = 36 + 47$
   ⬭ $+ 47 = 36 +$ ⬭

4. $(50 + 13) + 82 = 63 + 82$
   ⬭ $+$ ⬭ $=$ ⬭

Hands On: Expressions with All Four Operations

Problem of the Day ————————————— KEY NS 3.0

Tran earns $7 an hour working at the pet store. How much money would Tran make if he works 4 hours?

Number Sense ———————————————— KEY NS 3.0

On your whiteboard, write two multiplication and division fact families which include the number 6.

Word of the Day ———————————————— AF 1.0

properties

How are the *properties* for addition and multiplication similar?
How are they different?

_____

_____

_____

Facts Practice ———————————————— KEY AF 1.3

Add parentheses to make the value of each expression equal to 8.

1. $12 - 7 + 3$

2. $20 - 4 + 8$

3. $10 - 1 + 1$

4. $18 - 13 + 3$

5. $11 - 1 + 2$

Hands On: Expressions with All Four Operations

Use the numbers and operation symbols below to make an expression with the value of 4. Remember to follow the order of operations.

1. | 6 | | 2 | | 1 | | × | | − |

_____

2. | 8 | | 2 | | 0 | | ÷ | | + |

_____

3. | 1 2 | | 4 | | 2 | | × | | − |

_____

Write the expression shown below three times. Add one set of parentheses to each expression to get three different values.

$$6 + 4 \div 2 \times 6 - 3$$

4. _____

5. _____

6. _____

Writing Math Which expression from problems 4–6 has the same value as the expression without parentheses? Tell the order of the operations you did to get the same answer.

_____

_____

_____

_____

Hands On: Expressions with All Four Operations

Problem of the Day

Explain each step in solving the problem shown below.

$(7 + 8) \div 3 \times 4 - 2$

Number Sense

Write and solve a subtraction problem in which the thousands need to be regrouped as hundreds and the tens need to be regrouped as ones.

Number of the Day

12

Write all the ways 12 can be the answer to a multiplication problem.

_____

_____

_____

Facts Practice

Write each number in word form.

1. 54,291   **2.** 320,670   **3.** 759,781

4. 10,800,450   **5** 553,781,000

Expressions with All Four Operations

CA Standards
KEY AF 1.2, KEY AF 1.3

Simplify each expression. Follow the order of operations.

1. $(6 + 3) \times 4$

_____

2. $(7 - 5) \times 6$

_____

3. $(15 + 3) \div 6$

_____

4. $8 + (5 \times 3)$

_____

5. $9 - (21 \div 7)$

_____

6. $3 \times (12 - 8)$

_____

7. $7 + (6 \times 3) - 10$

_____

8. $30 - (3 \times 3) + 4$

_____

9. $(18 - 3) \div 5$

_____

10. $6 + 5 \times 4 - 7$

_____

11. $18 + 9 \times 7 - 13$

_____

12. $5 \times (6 + 3) \times 2$

_____

Write an expression for each situation.

13. the sum of 21 and the product of 8 and 7 _____

14. 73 more than 6 times 9 _____

15. 3 fewer than 42 divided by 7 _____

Test Practice

Circle the letter of the correct answer.

16. Karen owns 3 guitars that have 6 strings each and 2 mandolins that have 8 strings each. How many strings do her instruments have in all?

A 34   C 19

B 36   D 5

17. There are 30 students in the classroom. If three groups of 4 students leave the room, how many students are left?

A 26   C 12

B 18   D 20

18. David owns 4 guitars with 6 strings each and a guitar with 4 main strings and 22 special resonating strings. How would you find how may strings his instruments have in all?

_____

_____

Name _____ Date _____

Equations and Inequalities with All Four Operations

Problem of the Day

Write an expression to represent the phrase given below.
Then solve the expression.

Seven less than three times the sum of 5 and 4.

Number Sense

On your whiteboard write 3 different numbers which round
to 91,000.

Number of the Day

45

What are some ways to show 45?

_____

_____

_____

Facts Practice

Find each sum.

1. $648 + 827$

2. $859 + 61 + 571$

3. $1,958 + 487$

4. $4,782 + 8,391$

5. $40,549 + 281,391$

6. $200,391 + 589,891$

Equations and Inequalities with All Four Operations

CA Standard
AF 1.0

Copy and complete. Use >, <, or =.

1. $2 \times 3 \times 5 \bigcirc 90 \div 3$

2. $10 + 6 \times 8 \bigcirc 63 - 5$

3. $81 \div 9 + 4 \bigcirc 6 \times 2 + 5$

4. $\frac{60}{12} - 1 \bigcirc 3 + 2 \times 1$

5. $86 \bigcirc 13 \times 4 + 28$

6. $40 \div 5 \times 2 \bigcirc 30 - 18$

7. $7 \times 8 \div 2 \bigcirc 4 \times 8 + 6$

8. $4 \times 6 + 7 \bigcirc 62 \div 2$

Write +, −, ×, or ÷ in each $\bigcirc$ to make each number sentence true.

9. $3 \times 4 = 20 \bigcirc 8$

10. $5 \bigcirc 5 = \frac{18}{3} + 4$

11. $6 + 1 - 2 = 30 \bigcirc 5 - 1$

12. $7 \bigcirc 3 = 30 - 9$

Writing Math Roger changed one operation sign on each side of the equation in problem 1, in order to go from = to <. Was his math correct? What did he change the sign to?

_____

Multiply Equals by Equals

Problem of the Day ————————————————————— KEY AF 1.3

James wrote a 4 page story. Latisha wrote 1 more than 3 times as many pages as James. Jorge wrote 7 more pages than James. Write a number sentence to compare the number of pages Latisha wrote to the number Jorge wrote.

Number Sense ————————————————————— KEY NS 3.0

Write 5 basic multiplication facts which involve the number 8.

Word of the Day ————————————————————— MR 3.3

remainder

Give some examples of when you might have a *remainder* in real life.

_____

_____

_____

Facts Practice ————————————————————— AF 1.0

Use multiplication properties and division rules to find each missing number.

1. $45 \times 3 = 3 \times$ ____

2. $(8 \times 5) \times 9 = 8 \times ($ ____ $\times 9)$

3. ____ $\times 99 = 0$

4. $113 \times$ ____ $= 113$

5. $49 \div 49 =$ ____

6. $0 \div 5 =$ ____

Multiply Equals by Equals

Copy and complete.

1. $(4 + 6) \times$ _____ $= 10 \times 5$

2. $30 - (3 \times 9) = 30 -$ _____

3. _____ $\div 8 + 11 = 4 + 11$

4. $12 \times ($ _____ $- 3) = 12 \times 3$

5. $7 \times (24 \div 3) = 7 \times$ _____

6. _____ $\times (6 \times 7) = 4 \times 42$

7. $3 + 63 \div 9 = 3 +$ _____

8. $5 \times (8 - 3) = 5 \times$ _____

Test Practice

Circle the letter of the correct answer.

9. Fran multiplied one side of an equation by 12. How much must she multiply the other side by to keep the equation true?

   A 6   **C** 10

   B 12   **D** 24

10. Carl multiplied one side of an equation by 5. To make it an inequality, what must he multiply the other side by?

    A 5   **C** a number

    B $(2 + 3)$ **D** any number but 5

Writing Math Kelly multiplied one side of an equation by 6 and the other side by $(36 \div 6)$. Does she still have an equation? Explain.

Problem Solving: Write an Expression

Problem of the Day ————————————————— AF 2.0

**Write all the pairs of numbers that can be written in the blanks
below to make the equation true.**

$6 \times (14 + 7) = 21 \times (\_\_ + \_\_)$

Number Sense ————————————————— KEY NS 1.2

What place value would you need to change to make 539,138 greater
than 540,502?

Word of the Day ————————————————— MR 2.3

operation

Which numerical *operation* do you use most often during a day? Give
some examples of how you use it.

_____

_____

_____

Facts Practice ————————————————— KEY NS 1.1

Write each number in standard form.

1. 40,000 + 5,000 + 90 + 8

2. 100,000 + 7,000 + 500 + 80 + 2

3. 10,000 + 6,000 + 20

4. 2,000,000 + 300,000 + 8,000 + 800 + 30 + 1

5. 5,000,000 + 300,000 + 90,000 + 4

6. 3,000,000 + 7,000 + 600 + 40 + 3

Name _____ Date _____

Problem Solving:
Write an Expression

CA Standards
MR 2.4, **KEY** AF 1.3

Use the table for Problems 1–4. Write an equation to solve each problem.

Ben's Points	
Game	**Points**
1	8
2	12
3	6
4	18
Total	44

1. In Game 4, Ben scored half of his team's total points. How many points did his team score in Game 4?

   _____

2. Ben's friend Jason scored 3 fewer points than Ben did in Game 1, and 2 fewer points than Ben in Game 2. How many total points did Jason score in Games 1 and 2?

   _____

3. Ben scored an equal amount of points in Games 5 and 6. Ben's points in Game 5 equaled the total amount of points he scored in Games 3 and 4. How many total points did Ben score in Games 5 and 6?

   _____

4. Ben's team, including Ben, scored a total of 141 points in the first four games. How many points did Ben's teammates score in the first 4 games?

   _____

Test Practice

Circle the letter of the correct answer.

5. Martin is on Ben's team. In Games 1 and 2 he scored half the points Ben did. In Game 3 he scored one more point than Ben, and in Game 4 he scored 0 points. Which expression will Martin use to find out how many points he scored in all four games?

   A $(8 + 12) \div 2 + (6 + 1)$

   B $12 + 8 \div 2 - 6$

   C $(18 - 12) \times 2 + (6 + 1)$

   D $12 - 8 \div 2 + (6 + 1)$

Name _____ Date _____

Hands On: Variables

Problem of the Day

Tickets for a matinee movie are $6. Popcorn costs $2 a bucket and juice costs $1. Jamie and two friends went to the movie and each had a bucket of popcorn and a juice. Write an expression to represent the amount of money spent. Then solve the problem.

Algebra and Functions

Use properties and rules to solve. If there is no answer, explain why.

1. $7 + 3 = $ ___ $+ 7$

2. $5 \times (2 \times 8) = (5 \times 2) \times$ ___

3. $7 \div 0 = $ ___

4. $18 \times$ ___ $= 0$

Word of the Day

evaluate

Write a sentence that uses the word *evaluate*.

_____

_____

_____

Facts Practice

Divide.

1. $58 \div 7$

2. $23 \div 5$

3. $65 \div 8$

4. $86 \div 9$

5. $52 \div 8$

Name _____ Date _____

Hands On: Variables

CA Standards
AF 1.0, AF 1.1

Evaluate each expression.

1. $(a - 3) + 4$ when $a = 7$ _____

2. $(3 \times m) + (9 \times m)$ when $m = 1$ _____

3. $(10 \times r) + 5$ when $r = 4$ _____

4. $s - 9$ when $s = 45$ _____

5. $16 \div a$ when $a = 4$ _____

6. $g \times (g - 2)$ when $g = 6$ _____

7. $20 \div k$ when $k = 2$ _____

8. $c + (c + 2) + (c + 3)$ when $c = 0$ _____

Test Practice

Circle the letter of the correct answer.

9. Which of the following is $3 \times a + 5$ when $a = 4$?

   A 4   **C** 17

   B 27   **D** 60

10. Which number will give the smallest value of $3 \times m - 1$?

   A $m = 2$ **C** $m = 3$

   B $m = 4t$ **D** $m = 5$

Writing Math Marcella has p paintings and Giovanna has $4p$ paintings. If Marcella has 20 paintings, how many does Giovanna have? Explain how you know.

_____

_____

Name _____ Date _____

Write and Evaluate Algebraic Expressions

Problem of the Day ——————————————— KEY

Evaluate the expression $(y + 2) \times 8$ when $y = 7$ and $y = 5$.

Mathematical Reasoning ——————————————— MR 2.3

Explain how the number sentence $7 \times 9 = 63$ can be used to help find the answer to $63 \div 7 =$ _____.

Number of the Day ——————————————— KEY

2

What are the different ways to say 2 when writing an expression in words?

_____

_____

_____

Facts Practice ——————————————— KEY NS 3.0

Multiply.

1. 18×2 2. 30×5 3. 16×8

4. 17×7 5. 5×24 6. 6×51

Name _____ Date _____

Write and Evaluate Algebraic Expressions

CA Standards
AF 1.0, AF 1.1

Write an expression that matches the words.

1. a number plus six _____

2. three times a number plus four _____

3. twenty more than a number divided by six _____

4. four times one less than a number _____

Evaluate each expression when $b = 7$

5. $b + 2$ _____

6. $(11 - b) \times 20$ _____

7. $14 \div b + 9$ _____

8. $(b + 12) \times (b - 4)$ _____

Test Practice

Circle the letter of the correct answer.

9. Georgia has some paint tubes in her painting studio. She has 7 more paint tubes at home. Which expression shows Georgia's total number of paint tubes?

   A $7p$ **C** $7 + p$

   B $7 - p$ **D** $p - 7$

10. Which expression represents "five times two less than a number"?

    A $5(x - 2)$ **C** $5(2 - x)$

    B $10 - x$ **D** $2x - 5$

Writing Math Darnell and Taquasia are writing expressions for "two times three more than the number of calculators." Darnell writes $2 \times (3 + c)$. Taquasia writes $2 \times (c + 3)$. Explain why both students are correct.

_____

_____

Solve Addition and Subtraction Equations

Problem of the Day ──────────────── AF 1.0

Jayson has *n* number of baseball cards. Sam has three times the number of baseball cards as Jayson. Write an expression to represent the number of baseball cards Sam has. Then evaluate the expression if $n = 20$.

Algebra and Functions ──────────────── KEY AF 1.2

Write $>$, $<$ or $=$ for each ⬤.

1. $(13 \times 6) \times 2$ ⬤ $18 + (3 \times 2)$

2. $(6 \times 5) \div 2$ ⬤ $15 - (3 + 1)$

3. $7 \times 8 - 2$ ⬤ $9 \times 3 \times 2$

4. $3 \times (8 + 2)$ ⬤ $4 \times (7 - 1)$

Word of the Day ──────────────── KEY AF 1.1

solution

A solution is an answer to a problem. What is the solution to an equation? Why is it necessary to substitute the solution back into the equation?

_____

_____

_____

Facts Practice ──────────────── KEY AF 1.2

Simplify each expression.

1. $50 - 8 \times 2$

2. $(10 + 15) \div (3 + 2)$

3. $8 + 7 - 9 \div 3$

4. $(15 - 27 \div 9) + 5$

5. $(3 + 5) \times (2 \times 3)$

6. $(9 \div 3) \div (2 + 1)$

Solve Addition and Subtraction Equations

CA Standards
KEY AF 2.0, **KEY** AF 2.1

Solve the equation. Check the solution.

1. $y + 10 = 30$ _____

2. $p - 8 = 11$ _____

3. $n + 22 = 88$ _____

4. $3 + p = 90$ _____

5. $f + 99 = 200$ _____

6. $s - 320 = 300$ _____

7. $v - 100 = 22$ _____

8. $9 + x = 71$ _____

Test Practice

Circle the letter of the correct answer.

9. Marielle has ten more posters than Katherine. If Marielle has 45 posters, how many posters does Katherine have?

A 10   **C** 35

B 45   **D** 55

10. Shayna and Phoebe are comparing their math scores. If Phoebe received a 94 and Shayna scored 4 points less than Phoebe, what was Shayna's score?

A 4   **C** 90

B 94   **D** 98

Writing Math Blanche has 4 fewer books than Rhoda. Blanche has 12 books. How many books does Rhoda have? Write and solve an equation.

_____

Name _____ Date _____

Solve Multiplication and Division Equations

Problem of the Day ——————————————— AF 1.1

Julie and Mike time themselves to see how many math problems they can complete in one minute. They complete 45 problems altogether. Mike completes 22 problems. How many problems did Julie complete?

Number Sense ——————————————— KEY NS 3.0

Find the missing number.

1. $8 \times \underline{\hspace{1cm}} = 48$

2. $7 \times \underline{\hspace{1cm}} = 63$

3. $\underline{\hspace{1cm}} \times 3 = 21$

4. $12 \times \underline{\hspace{1cm}} = 72$

Word of the Day ——————————————— MR 2.3

inverse

Inverse means opposite. What is the inverse of walking to the right? What is the inverse of walking down stairs?

_____

_____

_____

Facts Practice ——————————————— KEY AF 1.2

Evaluate for $x = 3$.

1. $3x$

2. $15 \div x$

3. $x + 5$

4. $(x + 2) \times 8$

5. $(13 \times x) \div 2$

6. $x \times x + 5$

Solve Multiplication and Division Equations

CA Standards
KEY AF 2.0, KEY AF 2.2

Solve the equation. Check the solution.

1. $3a = 30$ _____

2. $4x = 88$ _____

3. $c \times 12 = 1{,}200$ _____

4. $5p = 55$ _____

5. $d \div 10 = 13$ _____

6. $14p = 42$ _____

7. $m \div 6 = 90$ _____

8. $100q = 4{,}200$ _____

Test Practice

Circle the letter of the correct answer.

9. Jake has 4 times as many quarters as Nick. If Jake has 20 quarters how many does Nick have?

   A 4   **C** 5

   B 20   **D** 80

10. Dorothea lives twice as far from school as Michaela. If Dorothea lives 4 miles from school, how far away from schools does Michaela live?

    A 2 miles   **C** 4 miles

    B 6 miles   **D** 8 miles

Writing Math Johnny has five times as many pennies as Liana. Johnny has 40 pennies. How many pennies does Liana have? Write and solve an equation.

_____

Problem Solving: Using Equations for Comparison Problems

Problem of the Day

KEY AF 2.0

A mail carrier delivers 105 newspapers to 7 different buildings. Each building receives the same number of newspapers. Write and solve an equation to find the number of newspapers that are delivered to each building.

Algebra and Functions

AF 1.0

Evaluate each expression for $n = 7$.

1. $3 \times n + 2$

2. $4 \times (n + 8)$

3. $n \div 1 + 5$

4. $6 \times n \div 3$

Number of the Day

MR 2.3

12

What kinds of things come in sets of 12?

_____

_____

_____

Facts Practice

NS 2.1

Estimate the sum to the nearest hundred.

1. $763 + 448$

2. $1,672 + 1,433$

3. $1,892 + 5,672$

4. $3,872 + 4,119$

5. $501 + 732 + 192$

6. $688 + 302 + 445$

Name _____ Date _____

Problem Solving: Use Equations for Comparison Problems

CA Standards
MR 2.3, **KEY** AF 2.0

Mariah asked the fourth graders in her school, "What is the best first pet to have?" The table shows the answers she collected. Use the information from the table to answer the questions. Write an equation to solve each problem. Use *u* for the unknown amount.

Sunset School Fourth Graders Best First Pets	
hamsters	16
guinea pigs	12
rabbits	8
gerbils	6
white mice	2

1. How many more fourth graders thought guinea pigs were better first pets than white mice?

   _____

2. How many more fourth graders thought rabbits were better first pets than gerbils?

   _____

3. Most of the fourth graders said hamsters were the best first pets. How many more fourth graders choose hamsters than choose rabbits and gerbils?

   _____

Test Practice

Circle the letter of the correct answer.

4. Mariah asked fifth graders the same question. Five times more fifth graders than fourth graders chose rabbits. Which equation will tell how many fifth graders chose rabbits?

   A $u \div 5 = 8$ **B** $u + 5 = 8$ **C** $8 + 5 = u$ **D** $5 \times 5 = u$

5. Nine more fifth graders than fourth graders chose hamsters as the best first pet. Which equation will tell how many fifth graders chose hamsters?

   A $9u = 16$ **B** $16u = 9$ **C** $u = 16 - 9$ **D** $u = 9 + 16$

Use with text pp. 180–181

Name _____ Date _____

Hands On: Function Tables

Problem of the Day

Tyson owns six times more shirts than he does pants. If he owns 18 shirts, how many pairs of pants does he own? Write an equation to solve the problem.

Number Sense

Use Workmat 4 to order the following numbers and list them from greatest to least.

45,054,504   45,054,405   45,504,450

Word of the Day

square number

What is special about a *square*? When you make an array for a *square number*, in what shape is the array?

_____

_____

_____

Facts Practice

Copy and complete.

1. $(3 \times 12) \times 4 = \bigcirc \times 4$

2. $8 \times (5 + 3) = \bigcirc \times 8$

3. $6 \times \bigcirc = (3 \times 2) \times 12$

4. $11 \times \bigcirc = 11 \times (13 - 7)$

5. $(2 \times 12) \times 7 = 24 \times \bigcirc$

6. $(5 \times 9) \times \bigcirc = \bigcirc \times 6$

Hands On: Function Tables

Use the pattern to complete the function table.

Figure 1   Figure 2   Figure 3

	Figure Number	Number of Squares
1.	1	
2.	2	
3.	3	
4.	4	
5.	5	
6.	6	

Test Practice

Circle the letter of the correct answer.

A school library is creating displays for National Library Week. The library is using 6 shelves to show special books. On each shelf, students are arranging 8 books. Complete the function table to show how many books there are on the shelves.

Number of Shelves	Number of Books
1	
2	
3	
4	
5	
6	

7. How many books are displayed on 3 shelves?

A 8   C 16

B 24   D 32

8. How many books are displayed on all 6 shelves?

A 32   C 40

B 48   D 54

Writing Math Create your own pattern. Make and complete a function table to match the pattern you have made.

Write Function Rules Using One Variable

Problem of the Day ———————————————— KEY **AF 1.5**

Complete the function table to find out how many pencils would be in
6 boxes.

Boxes	Pencils
1	8
2	16
3	24
4	32
5	
6	

Number Sense ———————————————— KEY **NS 3.1**

Write an example of the Associative Property of Addition.

Number of the Day ———————————————— AF 1.0

0

Can a number be divided by 0? Can 0 be divided by a number?

_____

_____

_____

Facts Practice ———————————————— KEY **AF 2.0**

Solve the equation.

1. $8 - p = 3$ **2.** $m + 7 = 28$ **3.** $5 = k - 6$

4. $45 = x + 19$ **5.** $y - 36 = 11$ **6.** $82 = 54 + w$

Write Function Rules Using One Variable

CA Standards
KEY AF 1.5, AF 1.1

Complete.

Rule: Output = 24 ÷ p

	Input (p)	Output
1.	2	
2.	6	
3.	12	

Rule: Output = 6 + 5d

	Input (d)	Output
4.	3	
5.	5	
6.	8	

7. Rule: _____

Input (v)	Output
5	15
9	27
14	42

Test Practice

Circle the letter of the correct answer.

Rule: Output = 4 + 7x

Input (x)	Output
3	25
5	
8	

8. What is the output value if the input value is 5?

A 16   C 35

B 39   D 48

9. What is the output value if the input value is 8?

A 19   C 45

B 59   D 60

Writing Math Why will the output values always be greater than the input values in the function table above?

_____

_____

_____

_____

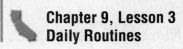
Write Function Rules Using Two Variables

Problem of the Day ———————————————————————— AF 1.1

What is the rule for the function table?

Input (*m*)	Output
4	1
7	4
10	7

Algebra and Functions ———————————————————— KEY AF 1.2

Is $28 - 9 + 2 - 11$ the same as $28 - (9 + 2) - 11$?

Number of the Day ———————————————————————— KEY NS 3.0

36

How many different arrays can be drawn for the number 36? List them all.

_____

_____

_____

Facts Practice ————————————————————————————— KEY NS 1.1

Write each number in word form.

1. 60,070,200

2. 874,900,049

3. 7,993,227

4. 20,007,001

Write Function Rules Using Two Variables

CA Standards
KEY AF 1.5, AF 1.1

Complete each function table or rule.

Rule: $b = a + 3$	
Input (a)	Output (b)
1. 5	
2. 8	
3. 3	

Rule: $y = 4x$	
Input (x)	Output (y)
4. 8	
5. 2	
6.	16

Rule: $t = s - 5$	
Input (s)	Output (t)
7. 13	
8.	13
9.	15

Rule: $g = k + 4$	
Input (k)	Output (g)
10. 2	
11. 8	
12.	13

13.
Rule:_____	
Input (x)	Output (y)
3	9
8	24
10	30

14.
Rule:_____	
Input (s)	Output (t)
3	1
15	5
21	7

Test Practice

Circle the letter of the correct answer.

15. If $y = 15 - x$ and $x = 7$, what is the value of y?

A 1   C 8

B 4   D 29

16. If $b = 32 - a$ and $a = 16$, what is the value of a?

A 2   C 8

B 15   D 16

Writing Math Jules worked 5 hours each day teaching drum lessons. Make a function table to show how many hours he worked in 1 day, 3 days, 7 days, and 11 days. Write an equation to show the rule.

Problem Solving: Field Trip

Problem of the Day ———————————— KEY

Complete the function table. **Rule:** $s = 5t + 2$

Input (t)	Output (s)
1	
4	
10	

Number Sense ———————————— KEY NS 3.2

How can you check that $37 \div 5 = 7$ R2?

Word of the Day ———————————— AF 1.1

variable

How does changing the number that the *variable* represents effect the value of the expression $(c + 5) \times 2$?

_____

_____

_____

Facts Practice ———————————— NS 2.1

Round each number to the nearest thousand. Then estimate the difference.

1. $34{,}502 - 3{,}338$

2. $7{,}390 - 2{,}612$

3. $91{,}834 - 49{,}755$

4. $645{,}035 - 8{,}489$

5. $120{,}630 - 104{,}377$

6. $550{,}421 - 24{,}923$

Hands On: Multiply 2-Digit Numbers by 1-Digit Numbers

Problem of the Day
MR 2.3

Kiana and Dane like to play checkers. Kiana wins 2 games each day for a week. Dane wins 3 games the first day and 1 game every day after that. Make a table to show how many games they played each day.

	Kiana	Dane	Total Games Played
Day 1			
Day 2			
Day 3			
Day 4			
Day 5			
Day 6			
Day 7			
TOTAL			

Number Sense
KEY **NS 1.1**

Use Workmat 2 to write the number in standard form.

twelve million, two hundred thirty one thousand, five hundred sixty three

Word of the Day
KEY **NS 3.0**

regroup

If you added 1,306 and 8,611, would you need to regroup the ones?

_____

_____

_____

Facts Practice
KEY **AF 2.0**

Solve the equation.

1. $4 \times p = 12$

2. $6 \times n = 12$

3. $6 \times d = 30$

4. $y \div 9 = 2$

5. $21 \div b = 7$

6. $20 \div x = 5$

Name _____ Date _____

Hands On: Multiply 2-Digit Numbers by 1-Digit Numbers

CA Standard
KEY NS 3.0

Tell what multiplication sentence the blocks show.

1.

_____

2.

_____

Use base-ten blocks to find the product.

3. $3 \times 28 =$ _____   **4.** $6 \times 13 =$ _____   **5.** $3 \times 15 =$ _____   **6.** $4 \times 17 =$ _____

Test Practice

Circle the letter of the correct answer.

7. Tennis balls are packaged three to a can. A box of tennis balls holds 12 cans. How many tennis balls are in one box?

   A 24   **C** 36

   B 30   **D** 42

8. There are three classes of fourth graders at Mason School. There are 24 students in each class. How many fourth graders attend Mason school?

   A 31   **C** 92

   B 72   **D** 96

 Writing Math How can you use base-ten blocks to multiply?

_____

_____

Estimate Products

Problem of the Day ————————————— KEY NS 3.0

Hadley's company sends 6 newsletters to 8 people. How many newsletters are sent?

Mathematical Reasoning ————————————— MR 2.3

Draw a quick picture on your whiteboard to show 7×9.

Word of the Day ————————————— MR 2.3

compare

If you are ordering numbers from least to greatest, do you need to compare the numbers? Explain your answer.

_____

_____

_____

Facts Practice ————————————— KEY NS 3.1

Subtract.

1. $1,384 - 1,068$ **2.** $41,099 - 7,763$ **3.** $61,987 - 44,322$

4. $306,116 - 179,185$ **5.** $700,004 - 318,911$

Estimate Products

Round the larger number to the greatest place. Then estimate the product.

1. 68
    × 4

2. 72
    × 9

3. 535
    × 3

4. 957
    × 3

5. 417
    × 2

6. 779
    × 8

7. 547
    × 5

8. 2,745
    × 7

9. 6,098
    × 7

10. 4,572
    × 2

11. 2,849
    × 4

12. 8,375
    × 3

13. 4 × 37

14. 5 × 98

15. 3 × 625

16. 2 × $39

_____

_____

_____

_____

17. 7 × 4590

18. 9 × 3,768

19. 6 × 5,245

20. 8 × 2,759

_____

_____

_____

_____

Test Practice

Circle the letter of the correct answer.

21. One hundred fifteen families each donated $5 to the children's charity during Kindness Week. Which is the best estimate of the amount of money the charity received?

    A $500   c $800

    B $700   D $1,200

22. Last year, 317 tickets were sold for the baseball game during Kindness Week. Twice as many tickets were sold this year. About how many tickets to the baseball game were sold this year?

    A 150   c 700

    B 600   D 800

Writing Math Is your estimate for Problem 22 lower or greater than the exact number? Explain.

_____

_____

Multiply Greater Numbers

Problem of the Day

The sixth graders need $800 for a trip. They held a talent show to raise money. They sold 213 tickets at $5 each. Explain if you need to estimate or calculate the exact answer to find if they have enough money.

Algebra and Functions

Write a function table with at least 4 pairs of values for the rule output $= 3n - 2$.

Word of the Day

greater

In what real-life situations might *greater* numbers be used?

_____

_____

_____

Facts Practice

Find each product.

1. 7×5 2. 9×3 3. 6×8

4. 4×9 5. 3×6 6. 8×7

Multiply Greater Numbers

CA Standards
KEY NS 3.0, MR 2.1

Multiply. Check by estimation.

1. 3,121
   × 3

2. $23.35
   × 2

3. 2,069
   × 4

4. 4,325
   × 5

5. 1,843
   × 6

6. $43.38
   × 8

7. 5,412
   × 7

8. 4,089
   × 3

9. $54.29
   × 5

10. 3,645
    × 4

11. 5,149 × 7 _____

12. 8,213 × 4 _____

13. 7,129 × 6 _____

14. $26.04 × 5 _____

 **Test Practice**

Circle the letter of the correct answer.

15. There are 5,280 feet in one mile. Jessica walks 4 miles each week. How many feet does she walk in one week?

    A 20,000 ft

    B 21,020 ft

    C 21,120 ft

    D 20,120 ft

16. Mr. Clark took a trip from Los Angeles to New York, then back to Los Angeles. The distance between Los Angeles and New York is 2,451 miles. How far did Mr. Clark travel in all?

    A 4,802 miles

    B 4,902 miles

    C 4,912 miles

    D 4,209 miles

Writing Math Compare multiplying money with multiplying non-money amounts.

_____

_____

_____

Multiply with Zeros

Problem of the Day
KEY NS 3.0

Glenville held a three-day festival. If an average of 3,425 people attended each day, how many people attended the festival in all?

Number Sense
NS 4.1

Write two factors less than 10 for the number 36.

Number of the Day
KEY NS 3.4

6,000

List three multiplication problems which if the factors were rounded would result in an estimate of 6,000.

_____

_____

_____

Facts Practice
KEY AF 2.0

Solve each equation for *n*.

1. $5n = 45$

2. $\frac{n}{7} = 7$

3. $23 + n = 41$

4. $n - 44 = 13$

Name _____ Date _____

Multiplying with Zeros

Multiply. Check by estimation.

1. 460
× 4

2. 708
× 2

3. 300
× 9

4. 4,077
× 3

5. 206
× 5

6. 907
× 6

7. 5,001
× 7

8. 6,030
× 8

9. 503 × 6

10. 660 × 4

11. 1,036 × 5

_____

_____

_____

12. 4,500 × 3

13. 3,130 × 7

14. 6,009 × 8

_____

_____

_____

 Test Practice

Circle the letter of the correct answer.
Multiply.

15. 6,073
×   8

A 48,564   **C** 49,364

B 48,584   **D** 49,454

16. 3,700
×   9

A 32,300   **C** 33,300

B 32,600   **D** 33,399

 Writing Math When you multiply 9,900 by any factor, what can you predict about the last two digits of the product?

_____

_____

Problem Solving: Field Trip

Problem of the Day ——————————————— KEY

Over the winter months, an online sports store sold 1,007 swimsuits.
During the spring and summer they sold 5 times as many swimsuits.
How many swimsuits did they sell in the spring and summer?

Number Sense ——————————————— KEY NS 3.1

Without actually subtracting, what place values will you need to
regroup to find 6,437 − 4,529?

Word of the Day ——————————————— MR 1.1

function

Give some examples of functional relationships.

_____

_____

_____

Facts Practice ——————————————— NS 2.1

Round to the nearest thousand to estimate each difference.

1. 4,592 − 3,412   **2.** 9,028 − 3,391   **3.** 24,903 − 17,356

4. 65,381 − 41,772   **5.** 40,657 − 25,358   **6.** 37,762 − 9,491

Hands On: Multiply by Multiples of 10

Problem of the Day

A delivery company charges by the number of items delivered in town. The equation $c = 4d$ shows the relationship between the cost c and the number of items delivered d. Make a function table to show how much it costs to deliver 1, 2, 3, and 4 packages in town.

Algebra and Functions

For each rule let the input n be 3. Find each output m.

1. $2n + 5 = m$　　　　**2.** $18 \div n = m$　　　　**3.** $5n - 8 = m$

Number of the Day

10

How many tens make 100? 200? 300?

_____

_____

_____

Facts Practice

Subtract.

1. $885 - 390$　　　　**2.** $708 - 352$　　　　**3.** $1,672 - 782$

Hands On: Multiply by Multiples of 10

CA Standards
KEY NS 3.0, KEY NS 3.3

Use basic facts and patterns to find the products.

1. $60 \times 5 =$ _____

$60 \times 50 =$ _____

$600 \times 50 =$ _____

$6,000 \times 50 =$ _____

2. $40 \times 8 =$ _____

$40 \times 80 =$ _____

$400 \times 80 =$ _____

$4,000 \times 80 =$ _____

3. $60 \times 7 =$ _____

$60 \times 70 =$ _____

$600 \times 70 =$ _____

$6,000 \times 70 =$ _____

4. $\begin{array}{r} 40 \\ \times\ 2 \\ \hline \end{array}$

5. $\begin{array}{r} 40 \\ \times\ 20 \\ \hline \end{array}$

6. $\begin{array}{r} 400 \\ \times\ 20 \\ \hline \end{array}$

7. $\begin{array}{r} 4,000 \\ \times\ 20 \\ \hline \end{array}$

8. $\begin{array}{r} 20 \\ \times\ 30 \\ \hline \end{array}$

9. $\begin{array}{r} 70 \\ \times\ 4 \\ \hline \end{array}$

10. $\begin{array}{r} 300 \\ \times\ 50 \\ \hline \end{array}$

11. $\begin{array}{r} 3,000 \\ \times\ 40 \\ \hline \end{array}$

12. $90 \times 3 =$

_____

13. $60 \times 90 =$

_____

14. $50 \times 50 =$

_____

15. $7,000 \times 40 =$

_____

Test Practice

Circle the letter of the correct answer.

16. One year, California farmers raised $1,000 \times 670$ sheep. How many sheep is that?

A 6,700

c 67,000

B 670,000

D 6,700,000

17. One year, Illinois farmers raised 100×690 sheep. How many sheep is that?

A 6,900

c 69,000

B 690,000

D 6,900,000

Writing Math When you multiply two factors ending in zeros, how many zeros are in the product?

_____

_____

_____

Hands On: Multiply 2-Digit Numbers by 2-Digit Numbers

Problem of the Day ———————————————— KEY **NS 3.3**

Use a pattern of zeros to find the products:

$40 \times 5 =$

$40 \times 50 =$

$40 \times 500 =$

$40 \times 5,000 =$

Algebra and Functions ———————————————— KEY **AF 2.0**

Solve each equation for n.

1. $3n = 12$

2. $n \div 5 = 7$

3. $3 + n = 9$

4. $14 = 7n$

Word of the Day ———————————————— NS 3.0

factor

Write all the factors for 36.

_____

_____

_____

Facts Practice ———————————————— KEY **AF 2.0**

Solve each equation for n.

1. $n + 3 = 5$

2. $4n = 12$

3. $n \div 5 = 9$

4. $n - 12 = 5$

5. $n - 3 = 8$

6. $n \times 5 = 30$

Name _____ Date _____

Hands On: Multiply 2-Digit Numbers by 2-Digit Numbers

CA Standards
AF 1.0, **KEY** NS 3.3

Use models and the Distributive Property to find each product. Record your work.

1. $12 \times 14 =$ _____

2. $13 \times 16 =$ _____

3. $18 \times 11 =$ _____

4. $11 \times 12 =$ _____

5. $21 \times 17 =$ _____

6. $24 \times 12 =$ _____

7. $20 \times 15 =$ _____

8. $13 \times 13 =$ _____

9. $14 \times 15 =$ _____

10. $22 \times 20 =$ _____

11. $31 \times 16 =$ _____

12. $19 \times 26 =$ _____

Test Practice

Circle the letter of the correct answer.

13. Mika made 25 bracelets. Each bracelet has 18 beads. How many beads did Mika use in all?

   A 420   C 450

   B 432   D 476

14. Chad swims 15 laps in the pool every day. How many laps does he swim in 27 days?

   A 405   C 435

   B 420   D 435

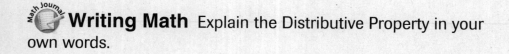

Writing Math Explain the Distributive Property in your own words.

_____

_____

Hands On: Multiply 2-Digit Numbers by 2-Digit Numbers

Problem of the Day ———————————————— KEY NS 1.3

There are 47 apartment buildings on a block. About how many apartment buildings are in an 18-block neighborhood?

Algebra and Functions ———————————————— KEY AF 2.0

Solve the equations.

1. $y - 3 = 4$

2. $4 + d = 12$

3. $z \times 6 = 12$

4. $p \div 8 = 3$

Number of the Day ———————————————— KEY NS 3.2

15

Multiply 15 by three different one-digit numbers.

_____

_____

_____

Facts Practice ———————————————— MR 1.1

Use patterns to multiply.

1. 40×100

2. 4×10

3. 10×100

4. 20×10

5. 7×100

Multiply 2-Digit Numbers by 2-Digit Numbers

CA Standards
KEY NS 3.2, KEY NS 3.3

Multiply.

1. $\begin{array}{r} 81 \\ \times\,22 \\ \hline \end{array}$

2. $\begin{array}{r} 57 \\ \times\,41 \\ \hline \end{array}$

3. $\begin{array}{r} 75 \\ \times\,28 \\ \hline \end{array}$

4. $\begin{array}{r} 63 \\ \times\,48 \\ \hline \end{array}$

5. $\begin{array}{r} 17 \\ \times\,14 \\ \hline \end{array}$

6. $\begin{array}{r} 63 \\ \times\,11 \\ \hline \end{array}$

7. $\begin{array}{r} 39 \\ \times\,24 \\ \hline \end{array}$

8. $\begin{array}{r} 45 \\ \times\,52 \\ \hline \end{array}$

9. 26×20 _____

10. 43×30 _____

11. 95×40 _____

12. 57×50 _____

13. 16×20 _____

14. 45×60 _____

15. 23×50 _____

16. 38×30 _____

Test Practice

Circle the letter of the correct answer.

17. Mrs. Reads's 32 fourth graders are making a quilt. Each student will sew 12 squares. How many squares will be in the quilt?

    A 284   C 285

    B 384   D 385

18. A total of 47 polar bears each ate 14 fish. How many fish did they eat in all?

    A 638   C 648

    B 658   D 748

 Writing Math When you multiply, when do you need to regroup?

_____

_____

Use with text pp. 238–240

Multiply 3-Digit Numbers by 2-Digit Numbers

Problem of the Day
KEY NS 3.2

A plant packages 35 bottles of tomato juice in each box. Boxes are
then gathered in groups of 28. How many bottles of tomato juice are
in each group?

Number Sense
KEY NS 1.2

Compare the following numbers using >, <, or =.

1. 169 ⬭ 196

2. 982 ⬭ 981

3. 2,574 ⬭ 2,547

4. 87,273 ⬭ 87,237

5. 212,904 ⬭ 212,904

6. 1,982,519 ⬭ 1,982,591

Word of the Day
KEY NS 3.0

product

Write two multiplication expressions with a product of 36.

_____

_____

Facts Practice
KEY NS 3.0

Multiply.

1. 58 × 6

2. 28 × 5

3. 134 × 6

4. 871 × 3

5. 2,981 × 6

6. 5,301 × 8

Multiply 3-Digit Numbers by 2-Digit Numbers

CA Standards
KEY NS 3.2, **KEY** NS 3.3

Multiply.

1. 242
   × 15

2. 307
   × 31

3. 123
   × 60

4. 584
   × 83

5. 221
   × 43

6. 418
   × 52

7. 395
   × 71

8. 600
   × 85

9. 86 × 472

10. 295 × 61

11. 24 × 975

12. 491 × 23

13. 502 × 59

14. 40 × 135

Test Practice

Circle the letter of the correct answer.

15. A factory makes 367 pairs of sneakers in 1 day. How many pairs of sneakers does it make in 26 days?

   A 8,142
   C 9,502
   B 9,532
   D 9,542

16. A factory makes 284 T-shirts in 1 day. How many T-shirts does it make in 14 days?

   A 2,676
   C 3,960
   B 3,968
   D 3,976

Writing Math Compare multiplying a 3-digit number by a 2-digit number with multiplying two 2-digit numbers.

_____

_____

_____

_____

Problem Solving: Guess and Check

Problem of the Day ———————————————————— KEY

Alan has twelve boxes with 23 books in each. How many books does he have?

Number Sense ———————————————————————— KEY

Multiply 56 times 4.

Word of the Day ———————————————————————— KEY AF 1.2

inequality

Write an inequality using multiplication.

_____

_____

_____

Facts Practice ———————————————————————— KEY

Add or subtract.

1. $413 + 227$ 2. $29 + 341$ 3. $669 - 232$

4. $45 + 60$ 5. $116 - 58$ 6. $92 - 33$

Problem Solving: Guess and Check

CA Standard
MR 1.0, **KEY** NS 3.3

Use Guess and Check to solve each problem.

Show Your Work.

1. Dave and Briana have a total of 82 CDs. Dave has 16 more CDs than Briana. How many CDs does each have?

_____

2. Matt is thinking of two numbers. One number is 9 more than the other number. The sum of the numbers is 45. What are the numbers?

_____

3. Together, Frank and Jules have played 24 shows. Jules has played three times as many shows as Frank has. How many shows has each of them played?

_____

4. Babs is thinking of two numbers. One number is 7 more than the other number. The product of the numbers is 60. What are the numbers?

_____

Test Practice

Circle the letter of the correct answer.

5. Ally and Jay have 59 video games. Jay has 13 more video games than Ally does. How many video games does Ally have?

   A 36   **C** 23

   B 46   **D** 49

6. Brandi has 6 pets, all cats and birds. Her pets have a total of 22 legs. How many cats and how many birds does Brandi have?

   A 1 bird, 5 cats   **C** 3 birds, 3 cats

   B 2 birds, 4 cats   **D** 4 birds, 2 cats

Hands On: Model Division

Problem of the Day

Use the guess-and-check method to solve this problem: Vanessa and her sister collect coins from foreign countries. Vanessa has 58 coins from foreign countries and her sister has 27. How many more coins do they need to collect to reach their goal of a combined total of 100 coins?

Number Sense Review

Jackson, Melissa, Rita, and Peng kept track of the number of pages that they each read during the month. The page numbers read were 157, 389, 215, and 503. About how many pages did they read altogether? Round each number to the nearest ten. Then find the total number of pages.

Number of the Day

46

What are some ways you can show 46?

_____

_____

_____

Facts Practice

Add or subtract mentally.

1. $27 + 2$ 2. $86 - 51$ 3. $35 + 34$

4. $94 - 10$ 5. $63 + 11$ 6. $47 - 27$

Name _____ Date _____

Hands On: Model Division

Use base-ten blocks to complete the table.

	Number	Number of Equal Groups	Number in Each Group	Number Left	Number Sentence
	14	2	7	0	$14 \div 2 = 7$
1.	29	7			
2.	35	5			
3.	75		9		
4.	25		8		
5.	63	9			

6. Draw a picture to show 17 divided into groups of 4 in each group. Write a number sentence to show division.

_____

Test Practice

Circle the letter of the correct answer.

7. If you divide 20 one-dollar bills into 4 equal groups how many one-dollar bills will be in each group?

   A 4   C 3

   B 5   D 1

8. Mr. Marris is building a birdhouse. He has 23 nails and 5 boards. If he hammers 4 nails in each board, how many nails will he have left over?

   A 2   C 3

   B 4   D 5

Writing Math Ron wanted to remove the remainder from problem 6 above. He decided to add 3 to the number being divided. Did this work? Explain.

_____

_____

Divide Larger Numbers with Remainders

Problem of the Day

Westwood Elementary School has 372 students. Sunrise Elementary School has 411 students. Rounding to the nearest hundred, about how many total students are there in both schools?

Number Sense Review

Use the number line below to name points A, B, C, D.

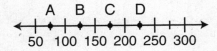

Word of the Day

regroup

Write an addition sentence in which you must regroup the ones.

_____

_____

_____

Facts Practice

Multiply.

1. 46×8 2. 7×55 3. 3×24

4. 94×8 5. 4×83 6. 31×5

Divide Larger Numbers with Remainders

CA Standards
KEY NS 3.2, KEY NS 3.0

Divide. Use multiplication to check.

1. $2\overline{)43}$ 2. $5\overline{)55}$ 3. $4\overline{)49}$ 4. $4\overline{)46}$ 5. $3\overline{)34}$

6. $5\overline{)54}$ 7. $4\overline{)47}$ 8. $2\overline{)65}$ 9. $7\overline{)78}$ 10. $3\overline{)65}$

11. $42 \div 2 =$ 12. $79 \div 7 =$ 13. $64 \div 3 =$ 14. $64 \div 2 =$ 15. $42 \div 4 =$

_____   _____   _____   _____   _____

16. $69 \div 2 =$ 17. $51 \div 9 =$ 18. $53 \div 3 =$ 19. $73 \div 7 =$ 20. $86 \div 4 =$

_____   _____   _____   _____   _____

Test Practice

Circle the letter of the correct answer.

21. Find $67 \div 3$.

 A 20 R1   c 22 R1

 B 21 R1   D 23 R3

22. Marsha, Ashley, Peter and Dawn have 45 pieces of candy to share equally. Each person gets 11 pieces. How many pieces are left over?

 A 1   c 3

 B 2   D 4

Writing Math Jan has 38 baseball caps. She put them in groups of 3 caps each and had 1 cap left over. Is she correct? Why or why not?

_____

_____

Hands On: Regroup in Division

Problem of the Day
KEY NS 3.4

If Mrs. Jessup wants to sit 5 students at a table and she has 32
students in her class, how many tables will she need?

Number Sense Review
KEY NS 1.1

Use Workmat 2 to write the following number in standard form: one
million, four hundred thirteen thousand, six hundred twenty.

Number of the Day
KEY NS 3.2

55

Divide this number two ways so that you do not get a remainder.

_____

_____

_____

Facts Practice
KEY NS 3.0

Round numbers to the nearest 10. Then multiply.

1. 17×22

2. 31×58

3. 8×9

4. 3×249

Regroup in Division

CA Standards
KEY NS 3.2, KEY NS 3.0

Divide. Use multiplication to check.

1. 3)‾40   2. 5)‾68   3. 6)‾93   4. 4)‾84   5. 2)‾73

6. 2)‾96   7. 4)‾87   8. 2)‾37   9. 3)‾49   10. 3)‾76

11. 54 ÷ 4 =   12. 60 ÷ 5 =   13. 83 ÷ 7 =   14. 86 ÷ 7 =   15. 45 ÷ 4 =

_____   _____   _____   _____   _____

16. 67 ÷ 5 =   17. 49 ÷ 3 =   18. 57 ÷ 5 =   19. 88 ÷ 8 =   20. 42 ÷ 3 =

_____   _____   _____   _____   _____

Test Practice

Circle the letter of the correct answer.

21. Jason is trading baseball cards. He can get 1 pack of cards for 5 single cards. If Jason has 63 single cards to trade, how many packs can he get?

   A 5   C 10

   B 12   D 15

22. If you had 52 cookies to put into 4 bags, how many cookies would go into each bag?

   A 6   C 9

   B 12   D 13

Writing Math Three friends made 44 cupcakes. They shared the cupcakes evenly and each got 11 cupcakes with 2 left over. Is this answer correct? Which part is wrong and why?

_____

_____

Divide Multiples of 10

Problem of the Day
KEY NS 3.0

Cho has 96 collectible spoons he wants to display equally in four cases. How many spoons will go in each case?

Algebra and Functions Review
KEY AF 1.5

Use Workmat 3 to create a function table for the rule $y = 3x + 1$, using 1, 2, 3, and 4 for input values.

Word of the Day
KEY NS 3.2

remainder

What is the *remainder* in each problem?

1. $2,356 \div 5$ **2.** $3,938 \div 4$ **3.** $6,714 \div 9$

_____

_____

_____

Facts Practice
KEY NS 3.0

Multiply.

1. 345×7 **2.** $1,928 \times 3$ **3.** $5,217 \times 6$

4. 999×4 **5.** $6,431 \times 2$ **6.** 782×5

Divide Multiples of 10

CA Standards
KEY NS 3.2, MR 1.1

Divide. Use multiplication to check.

1. $8 \div 2 =$ _____

$80 \div 2 =$ _____

$800 \div 2 =$ _____

2. $6 \div 3 =$ _____

$60 \div 3 =$ _____

$600 \div 3 =$ _____

3. $5 \div 1 =$ _____

$50 \div 1 =$ _____

$500 \div 1 =$ _____

4. $45 \div 5 =$ _____

$450 \div 5 =$ _____

$4,500 \div 5 =$ _____

5. $10 \div 2 =$ _____

$100 \div 2 =$ _____

$1,000 \div 2 =$ _____

6. $15 \div 5 =$ _____

$150 \div 5 =$ _____

$1,500 \div 5 =$ _____

7. $480 \div 6 =$ _____

8. $2,700 \div 3 =$ _____

9. $600 \div 2 =$ _____

Solve each equation.

10. $2,100 \div 3 = n$

11. $160 \div 4 = x$

12. $350 \div 5 = y$

13. $48 \div 6 = q$

_____ _____ _____ _____

Test Practice

Circle the letter of the correct answer.

14. Which number sentence is NOT correct?

A $240 \div 4 = 60$ C $250 \div 5 = 50$

B $2,800 \div 4 = 700$ D $700 \div 2 = 1,400$

15. A giant panda may eat up to 420 pounds of food in a week. How many pounds of food can a panda eat in 1 day?

A 6   C 60

B 600   D 20

Writing Math What critical piece of information is not *directly* given in problem 15 that you need to know to successfully complete it?

_____

_____

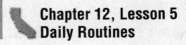
Problem Solving: Interpret Remainders

Problem of the Day KEY **NS 3.0**

Anita has a collection of 42 plastic bracelets. She would like to give them away to 5 friends. If she divides them equally, how many bracelets will Anita have left over?

Number Sense Review ———————————————— KEY **NS 1.3**

Round each of these numbers to the nearest 100:

855; 94; 1,672; 832

Word of the Day ——————————————————— MR 2.3

estimate

Give examples of things for which you may need to estimate.

_____

_____

_____

Facts Practice KEY **NS 3.0**

Multiply.

1. 12 × 11

2. 11 × 8

3. 7 × 9

4. 6 × 12

Problem Solving: Interpret Remainders

CA Standards
KEY NS 3.4, MR 1.0

Solve. Explain why your answer makes sense.

Show Your Work.

1. Gordan's Pineapple Farm in Hawaii is shipping 69 pineapples in wooden boxes. Each box holds 6 pineapples. How many boxes are needed?

   _____

   _____

2. Ms. Ramon brought 26 pineapples home from her vacation to Hawaii. She divided the pineapples into 3 equal piles and ate the pineapples that were left over. How many pineapples did Ms. Ramon eat?

   _____

3. Mr. Kelly's class has $65 to spend at the pineapple farm. Each pineapple costs $3. How many pineapples can the class buy?

   _____

4. Mr. Jack's class helps pack pineapples into shipping boxes. The class is given 94 pineapples to pack. Each shipping box holds 9 pineapples. How many boxes can the class fill?

   _____

Test Practice

Circle the letter of the correct answer.

5. At the grocery store, Alice is arranging pineapples in the produce case. She puts 7 pineapples in each row, one at a time. What row does she put the 29th pineapple in?

   A row 3   **C** row 4

   B row 5   **D** row 6

6. The school cafeteria needs to buy 50 pineapples. The pineapples come in boxes of 6. How many boxes should they buy?

   A 6 boxes   **C** 7 boxes

   B 8 boxes   **D** 9 boxes

Hands On: Model Division: 3-Digit Dividends

Problem of the Day ——————————————————— MR 1.0

There are 79 fourth graders. The gym teacher divides the fourth graders into 5 groups for field day. The students not in a group are the referees. How many students are referees? What part of the answer does this represent?

Number Sense ——————————————————— KEY NS 3.2

On your whiteboard, write a division problem which has a two digit dividend and will have a remainder. Trade whiteboards with another student and solve each other's problems.

Word of the Day ——————————————————— MR 2.3

greater

Use the words *greater than* to describe something in your school.

_____

_____

_____

Facts Practice ——————————————————— KEY NS 3.0

Divide.

1. $92 \div 4$ **2.** $87 \div 3$ **3.** $64 \div 5$

4. $79 \div 3$ **5.** $95 \div 7$ **6.** $83 \div 6$

Name _____ Date _____

Hands On: Model Division: 3-Digit Dividends

CA Standards
KEY NS 3.4, MR 2.3

For each quotient, write the number of each base-ten block that is in each group.

1. 639 divided by 3

   Number of Hundreds Blocks in Each Group _____

   Number of Tens Blocks in Each Group _____

   Number of Ones Blocks in Each Group _____

   Leftover Ones Blocks _____

   Quotient _____

2. 707 divided by 7

   Number of Hundreds Blocks in Each Group _____

   Number of Tens Blocks in Each Group _____

   Number of Ones Blocks in Each Group _____

   Leftover Ones Blocks _____

   Quotient _____

Test Practice

Circle the letter of the correct answer.

3. What is the remainder when 321 is divided by 3?

   A 0   **C** 1

   B 2   **D** 3

4. Divide $5\overline{)635}$.

   A 105   **C** 127

   B 150   **D** 170

Writing Math When number blocks are used to divide 644 by 6, there are no tens blocks in each equal grouping. Explain why this is true.

_____

_____

_____

3-Digit Quotients

Problem of the Day

Jesse wants to give out stickers from his sticker collection to 4 friends. He has 57 stickers in his collection. How many stickers does each friend get?

Number Sense

Round each number to the nearest thousand.

1. 1,567

2. 6,023

3. 8,501

4. 9,444

Word of the Day

KEY NS 3.0

dividend

Label the dividend in the following division problems:
4)36; 47 ÷ 3; 89 ÷ 8; 7)90.

_____

_____

_____

Facts Practice

Use patterns to multiply.

1. 10 × 78   2. 86 × 100   3. 100 × 29

4. 45 × 10   5. 10 × 100

3-Digit Quotients

CA Standards
KEY NS 3.4, **KEY** NS 3.0

Divide. Check your answers.

1. 6)639

2. 4)498

3. 2)783

4. 7)801

5. 3)642

6. 5)712

7. 3)858

8. 2)793

9. 428 ÷ 3

10. 543 ÷ 4

11. 945 ÷ 5

12. 674 ÷ 6

 **Test Practice**

Circle the letter of the correct answer.

13. 3)538

   A 112   C 119

   B 172 R2   D 179 R1

14. Which is the quotient of 185 divided by 5?

   A 37   C 37 R1

   B 38   D 38 R2

Writing Math Anna used 635 beads to make 5 bracelets. She put the same number of beads on each bracelet. Explain how many beads each bracelet has?

_____

_____

Place the First Digit of the Quotient

Problem of the Day

Yolanda needs to read a 620 page book in 5 days. How many pages must she read each day?

Algebra and Functions

Write a sentence and a function rule to represent the function table described below:

Number of Spiders	Number of Legs
1	8
2	16
3	24
4	32

Word of the Day

remainder

Can a remainder ever be greater than 9? Explain your answer.

_____

_____

_____

Facts Practice

Find each product.

1. 15 × 27

2. 49 × 83

3. 75 × 13

4. 280 × 21

5. 504 × 76

6. 30 × 453

Problem Solving: Field Trip

Problem of the Day ————————————— NS 4.1

What are the prime factors of 42?

Number Sense ————————————— KEY **NS 1.1**

Fill in the missing numbers.

1. 5,000 = ____ hundreds

2. 750 = ____ tens

3. 80,000 = ____ hundreds

4. 36,000 = ____ tens

Word of the Day ————————————— MR 2.0

strategy

Describe some Problem-Solving Strategies you use.

_____

_____

_____

Facts Practice ————————————— KEY **AF 1.3**

Simplify.

1. $8 - 5 + 2 \div 2$ **2.** $17 + (8 - 2) \div 2$ **3.** $35 \div 5 + 4$

4. $(19 - 1) \div (6 + 3)$ **5.** $15 + (16 \div 2 + 1)$ **6.** $3 \times 4 + 5 - 8$

Name _____ Date _____

Hands On: Measure Length

Problem of the Day ————————————————

Choose the best operation and solve.

Amy has three sets of stamps. Each set has 20 stamps. How many
stamps does she have?

Mathematical Reasoning ———————————————

On your whiteboard draw 7 groups of 6 squares. What multiplication
sentence represents the total number of squares?

Word of the Day —————————————————

factor tree

Using your whiteboard, make a factor tree for 20.

_____

_____

_____

Facts Practice ————————————————————

Divide.

1. $122 \div 4$ **2.** $246 \div 3$

3. $512 \div 7$ **4.** $313 \div 5$

Name _____ Date _____

Hands On: Measure Length

CA Standard
KEY NS 1.9

Measure each object to the nearest inch and nearest half inch.

1. _____

2. _____

3. _____

4. _____

5. _____

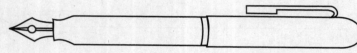

Test Practice

Circle the letter of the correct answer.

6. Estimate the length of a paperclip.

   A $\frac{1}{2}$ inch

   B 2 inches

   C $\frac{1}{4}$ inch

   D 5 inches

7. David measured two pencils. The first pencil measured $6\frac{1}{4}$ inches long. The second pencil measured $5\frac{3}{4}$ inches long. How long are the pencils, each measured to the nearest inch?

   A Both pencils are 11 inches long.

   B Both pencils are 12 inches long.

   C Both pencils are 6 inches long.

   D Both pencils are 5 inches long.

 Writing Math Explain where $1\frac{1}{2}$ inches is marked on a ruler.

_____

Perimeter and Customary Units of Length

Problem of the Day ————————————————————— KEY NS 1.9

Felipe is using a piece of ribbon for an art project. The ribbon measures between $7\frac{1}{2}$ and 8 inches. What is the length of the ribbon measured to the nearest inch?

Number Sense ————————————————————— KEY NS 3.4

In the following problem is the remainder the solution, is the remainder dropped in the solution, or is the quotient increased for the solution?

Rides on a fire engine are being given to a group of 186 fourth graders. If only 8 children can ride at one time, how many trips must be made so everyone can ride?

Number of the Day ————————————————————— KEY NS 4.2

2

The number 2 is the only even prime number. Why is this?

_____

_____

_____

Facts Practice ————————————————————— KEY NS 4.2

Write *prime* or *composite*.

1. 17

2. 24

3. 2

4. 51

5. 9

6. 5

Name _____ Date _____

Perimeter and Customary Units of Length

CA Standards
KEY NS 3.2, MG 1.0

Find the perimeter of each polygon.

1.

15 ft

_____

2.

8 in.

4 in.

_____

3.

9 ft

_____

Find the missing number.

Customary Units of Length
1 foot (ft) = 12 inches (in.)
1 yard (yd) = 3 feet
1 yard (yd) = 36 inches
1 mile (mi) = 5,280 feet
1 mile (mi) = 1,760 yards

4. 54 ft = _____ yd

5. 8,800 yd = _____ mi

6. 60 in. = _____ ft

7. _____ in = 3 yd

 Test Practice

Circle the letter of the correct answer.

8. The perimeter of a regular octagon is 32 in. What is the length of one side of the octagon?

A 32 in. **C** 24 in.

B 8 in. **D** 4 in.

9. A rectangular lawn is 45 feet long and 30 yards wide. What is its perimeter in yards?

A 270 yards **C** 225 yards

B 150 yards **D** 90 yards

Writing Math Terrance needs to know how many feet are in 3 miles. Tell him how to find the answer.

_____

_____

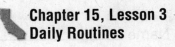
Customary Units of Capacity and Weight

Problem of the Day ————————————————————— KEY NS 3.2

Tessa cuts 5 feet from a ream of paper 3 yards long. How much paper is left?

Number Sense ————————————————————————— KEY NS 3.2

Write the multiplication and division fact family for 7 and 8.

Word of the Day ——————————————————————————— NS 2.1

estimate

Throughout the day, see how many times you see or hear people give estimates.

_____

_____

_____

Facts Practice ——————————————————————————— MR 2.3

Use patterns to multiply.

1. 4×6 **2.** 40×6 **3.** 40×60

4. 400×60 **5.** 400×600

Customary Units of Capacity and Weight

CA Standard
KEY NS 3.2

Find each missing number.

<table>
<tr><td>Customary Units of Capacity</td></tr>
</table>

1. 22 c = _____ pt

2. 11 gal = _____ qt

3. 16 pt = _____ qt

4. _____ c = 12 pt

5. 4 gal = _____ pt

6. 64 c = _____ gal

7. _____ qt = 6 gal

8. 3 gal = _____ c

Customary Units of Capacity
1 pint = 2 cups
1 quart = 2 pints
1 quart = 4 cups
1 gallon = 4 quarts
1 gallon = 8 pints
1 gallon = 16 cups

 Test Practice

Circle the letter of the correct answer.

9. Which amount is equal in capacity to 2 gallons?

   A 8 pints

   B 32 cups

   C 4 quarts

   D 16 quarts

10. Michael has 12 cups of water. Jenny has 5 pints of water. Liam has 4 quarts of water. Which choice lists these amounts in order from least to greatest capacity?

   A 12 cups, 5 pints, 4 quarts

   B 5 pints, 12 cups, 4 quarts

   C 4 quarts, 5 pints, 12 cups

   D 12 cups, 4 quarts, 5 pints

Writing Math Explain how to convert 16 quarts to gallons.

_____

_____

_____

Practice
146   Use with text pp. 332–333

Metric Units of Length

Problem of the Day

KEY **NS 3.2**

Ian and his friend Rico are trying to decide who is taller. Ian says he is
4 feet. Rico says he is 49 inches. Who is taller? How much taller?

Mathematical Reasoning

MR 2.3

On your whiteboard draw circles to represent 52 divided into 4
equal groups. What division sentence represents the total number
of circles in each group?

Number of the Day

KEY **NS 1.1**

10

Throughout the day, find things that are about 10 inches long.

_____

_____

_____

Facts Practice

KEY **NS 3.1**

Add.

1. $324 + 516$

2. $571 + 329$

3. $208 + 862$

4. $612 + 588$

Name _____ Date _____

Metric Units of Length

CA Standards
KEY NS 3.2, **KEY** AF 1.5

Find the missing number.

Metric Units of Length
1 centimeter = 10 millimeters (cm) (mm)
1 decimeter (dm) = 10 centimeters
1 meter (m) = 10 decimeters
1 kilometer (km) = 1,000 meters

1. 5,000 m = _____ km

2. 800 mm = _____ cm

3. 5 m = _____ cm

4. 80 km = _____ m

5. _____ dm = 70 cm

6. _____ mm = 4 cm

Complete the table. Write the rule using _x_ and _y_.

7. Rule: _____

Input: cm (_x_)	500	550	600	650	700
Output: dm (_y_)	50	55	**8.**	**9.**	**10.**

Test Practice

Circle the letter of the correct answer.

11. Jonathan's older brother dives from the 10-meter platform. How tall is the platform to the nearest decimeter?

   A 1 decimeter

   B 100 decimeters

   C 10 decimeters

   D 1,000 decimeters

12. His other brother dives from the 3-meter springboard. How far above the water is the springboard to the nearest centimeter?

   A 30 centimeters

   B 300 centimeters

   C 3,000 centimeters

   D 30,000 centimeters

Writing Math Do you think it is easier to convert customary units of length or metric units of lengths? Why?

_____

_____

_____

Name _____ Date _____

Metric Units of Capacity and Mass

Problem of the Day ———————————————————— KEY NS 3.2

Kelly wants to take oranges to soccer practice for her teammates. If there are 11 players on her team and each player will get 2 oranges, how many oranges should she bring to practice?

Number Sense ———————————————————— KEY NS 3.2

Write the fact family for $8 \times 5 = 40$.

Number of the Day ———————————————————— AF 1.1

variable

Write 2 equations that have a variable.

_____

_____

_____

Facts Practice ———————————————————— KEY AF 1.5

Solve each equation.

1. $5 \times y = 30$ **2.** $7 \times d = 63$ **3.** $b \times 11 = 55$

4. $f \times 8 = 64$ **5.** $10 \times d = 10$ **6.** $6 \times m = 0$

Name _____ Date _____

Metric Units of Capacity and Mass

CA Standards
KEY NS 3.2, MR 3.2

Find each missing number.

1. 6 L = _____ mL

2. 3,000 mL = _____ L

3. 5 L = _____ mL

4. 8,000 mL = _____ L

5. 10 L = _____ mL

6. _____ L = 20,000 mL

Choose the better estimate of capacity of each.

7.

   a. 20 mL   **b.** 2 L

8.

   a. 10 mL   **b.** 1 L

9.

   a. 200 mL   **b.** 20 L

10.

   a. 300 mL   **b.** 3 L

11.

   a. 40 mL   **b.** 40 L

12.

   a. 700 mL   **b.** 7 L

Test Practice

Circle the letter of the correct answer.

13. Which is the best estimate for the capacity of a jug of milk?

   A 2 L   **B** 2 mL   **C** 20 L   **D** 20 mL

14. Jessica has 12 bottles of water. Each bottle has a capacity of 750 mL. How many liters of water can the bottles hold?

   A 9 liters   **B** 90 liters   **C** 900 liters   **D** 9,000 liters

Writing Math Randy says that the carton of milk has a mass of 2 liters. What has he done wrong?

_____

_____

_____

Problem Solving: Estimated or Exact Amounts

Problem of the Day ————————————————— KEY NS 3.2

Izavella is washing her bike with a bucket of water that holds 9 liters of water. How many milliliters of water does the bucket hold?

Number Sense ————————————————————— KEY NS 3.4

Identify whether each quotient has two or three digits.

1. $585 \div 9$

2. $423 \div 3$

3. $664 \div 8$

Word of the Day ———————————————————— NS 4.1

factor

Does a square number have an even or an odd number of factors?

_____

_____

_____

Facts Practice ————————————————————— KEY NS 3.3

Multiply.

1. 36×12 **2.** 54×27 **3.** 76×49

4. 83×15 **5.** 65×91 **6.** 11×58

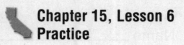
Problem Solving: Estimated or Exact Amounts

CA Standards
KEY NS 3.1, NS 2.1

The Hillsboro Elementary School had a bake sale to raise money for their class trip. The table shows how many of each item were sold. Solve each problem. Explain why you used estimates or exact numbers.

Bake Sale	
Item	**Number Sold**
Brownies	76
Cookies	135
Muffins	107
Banana Bread	85

1. Were there more than 400 items sold at the bake sale?

_____

_____

2. How many brownies and cookies were sold altogether?

_____

_____

3. About how many more cookies were sold than banana bread?

_____

_____

Test Practice

Circle the letter of the correct answer.

4. The students earned $214 selling muffins and $127.50 selling banana bread. About how much money is that?

   A $338   c $330

   B $340   D $350

5. The students raised a total of $628.50 with this bake sale. About how much more do they need to reach their goal of $1,500?

   A $800   c $900

   B $950   D $1,000

Writing Math Three different students got three different answers to problem 3 above. Can all of them be right? Why or why not?

_____

_____

Hands On: Negative Numbers on the Number Line

Problem of the Day ———————————————————————— KEY NS 1.4

Kiely and her parents are going on a trip. They can bring up to 390 pounds of luggage. Keily's bag weighs 45 pounds, her mom's bags weigh 96 pounds and her dad's bags weigh 153 pounds. Do Kiely and her parent's bags weigh too much? Did you use an estimate or an exact answer?

Number Sense ———————————————————————————— NS 4.1

Tran said all numbers ending in 3 are prime. Is he correct? List 3 examples to prove whether or not he is correct.

Number of the Day ———————————————————————— NS 1.0

10

Explain why the number ten is important in our place value system.

_____

_____

_____

Facts Practice ———————————————————————— KEY NS 3.2

Find the missing measures.

1. 48 in. = ____ ft   2. 3 yd = ____ ft   3. 2 mi = ____ ft

4. 6 ft = ____ in.   5. 72 in. = ____ yd   6. 4 yd = ____ in.

Name _____ Date _____

Hands On: Negative Numbers on the Number Line

Write the integer for the letter on the number line.

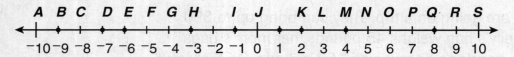

A B C D E F G H I J K L M N O P Q R S
−10 −9 −8 −7 −6 −5 −4 −3 −2 −1 0 1 2 3 4 5 6 7 8 9 10

1. C _____

2. O _____

3. J _____

4. H _____

Write the letter for the integer on the number line.

5. −9 _____

6. 3 _____

7. 9 _____

8. −4 _____

Circle the letter of the correct answer.

9. What is the opposite of −6?

A −12   C 6

B 0   D 12

10. What is the opposite of 10?

A −10   C 0

B −5   D 5

Writing Math How many integers are there from −4 to 4?
Explain your answer.

_____

_____

Compare Positive and Negative Numbers

Problem of the Day

KEY NS 3.0

Sofia and Maria want to buy a gift for their mother. Maria saves $7 for the gift and Sofia saves $9 for the gift. If you wanted to know how much money they can spend together, what operation would you use?

Number Sense

NS 2.2

A school hosted a food drive for some of the other schools in its district. Ten different schools participated. The schools collected the following number of food items: 610, 735, 833, 475, 350, 904, 466, 395, 588, and 754. About how many items were donated?

Word of the Day

KEY NS 1.8

integer

Give some examples of integers you might see during the day.

_____

_____

_____

Facts Practice

KEY NS 3.0

Complete each $\bigcirc$ using + or −.

1. $53 \bigcirc 42 = 11$ **2.** $26 \bigcirc 21 = 47$ **3.** $98 \bigcirc 2 = 100$

4. $78 \bigcirc 19 = 97$ **5.** $56 \bigcirc 10 = 46$ **6.** $17 \bigcirc 18 = 35$

Compare Positive and Negative Numbers

Use the number line and the symbols >, <, or = to complete the number sentence.

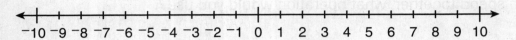

$$-10\ -9\ -8\ -7\ -6\ -5\ -4\ -3\ -2\ -1\ \ 0\ \ 1\ \ 2\ \ 3\ \ 4\ \ 5\ \ 6\ \ 7\ \ 8\ \ 9\ \ 10$$

1. $-8 \bigcirc -10$

2. $-5 \bigcirc -3$

3. $-1 \bigcirc -6$

4. $-2 \bigcirc -7$

5. $0 \bigcirc 0$

6. $-1 \bigcirc -1$

7. $-4 \bigcirc 1$

8. $-8 \bigcirc -2$

9. $-7 \bigcirc -10$

10. $0 \bigcirc -9$

11. $-8 \bigcirc 0$

12. $-3 \bigcirc -3$

Test Practice

Circle the letter of the correct answer.

13. At 6 A.M., the temperature was $-8°$.
At noon, the temperature was $-3°$.
At 6 P.M., the temperature was $-1°$.
At midnight, the temperature was $-10°$.
Which was the lowest temperature?

A $-8°$ **C** $-1°$

B $-3°$ **D** $-10°$

14. At 6 A.M., the temperature was $-8°$.
At noon, the temperature was $-3°$.
At 6 P.M., the temperature was $-1°$.
At midnight, the temperature was $-10°$.
Which temperature was closest to 0?

A $-8°$ **C** $-1°$

B $-3°$ **D** $-10°$

Writing Math How do you know that -2 is greater than -7?

_____

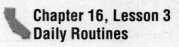
Use Negative Numbers

Problem of the Day ——————————————— KEY NS 1.8

On Monday, the temperature was –5°F. On Tuesday, the temperature
was 0°F. Which day had the higher temperature?

Mathematical Reasoning ——————————————— MR 1.1

Diana wrote a three digit number that was divisible by 3. The ones
digit was 4, the hundreds digit was less than the ones digit, and
the tens digit was greatest digit. Write the 3 numbers that fit this
description.

Word of the Day ——————————————— NS 1.0

compare

When you *compare* negative integers, what value are you comparing
them to? Explain your answer.

_____

_____

_____

Facts Practice ——————————————— KEY NS 1.2

Compare. Write >, <, or =.

1. 6,592 ◯ 6,500   **2.** 8,391 ◯ 9,120   **3.** 4,082 ◯ 4,028

4. 12,064 ◯ 12,064   **5.** 43,589 ◯ 43,587   **6.** 3,598,671 ◯ 3,598,760

Name _____ Date _____

Use Negative Numbers

CA Standards
KEY NS 1.8, NS 1.0

Use the number line to help you find the amount.

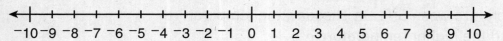

1. 1 more than ⁻5

_____

2. 2 fewer than 1

_____

3. 5 more than ⁻4

_____

4. 6 fewer than 6

_____

5. 7 fewer than 0

_____

6. 8 more than ⁻5

_____

7. 3 fewer than ⁻2

_____

8. 4 more than ⁻3

_____

9. 11 fewer than 1

_____

10. 10 more than ⁻9

_____

11. 8 more than ⁻9

_____

12. 5 fewer than ⁻5

_____

✓ Test Practice

Circle the letter of the correct answer.

13. The temperature was 4° and it dropped 5 degrees. What is the temperature now?

  A ⁻1°   **C** ⁻5°

  B 0°   **D** 9°

14. The temperature was ⁻6° and it rose 4 degrees. What is the temperature now?

  A ⁻10°   **C** 2°

  B ⁻2°   **D** 10°

Writing Math At the start of a game, you have 0 points. In the first round, you win 3 points. In the second round, you lose 2 points. Explain how many points you have now.

_____

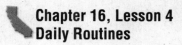
Problem Solving: Field Trip

Problem of the Day ———————————————— KEY

Sarah borrowed $12 from her mom. The next week she gave back her mom $4. How much money does Sarah still owe her mom? Explain how to use a number line to find the answer.

Measurement and Geometry ———————————————— MG 1.4

Find the width of the rectangle below.

Perimeter = 36 ft

12 ft

Number of the Day ———————————————— MR 1.1

12

Name several items which commonly come in groups of 12.

_____

_____

_____

Facts Practice ———————————————— NS 4.1

List all the factors of each number.

1. 18   **2.** 22   **3.** 35

4. 37   **5.** 48   **6.** 51

Hands On: Model Fractions

Problem of the Day

KEY **NS 1.4**

Gloria's science class is split into 5 different groups. Each group receives a box full of rocks. The groups are able to classify 25, 32, 47, 35, and 42 of their rocks. About how many rocks was the whole class able to classify?

Number Sense

KEY **NS 3.1**

Bridget bought three different types of lilies for $2.00 each. If she gave the cashier a $10 bill, what should her change be?

Number of the Day

NS 4.1

25

What are some ways to show 25?

_____

_____

_____

Facts Practice

KEY **NS 3.2**

Use a related multiplication fact to solve each problem.

1. 108 ÷ ☐ = 9   **2.** 100 ÷ ☐ = 10   **3.** 36 ÷ ☐ = 6

4. 77 ÷ ☐ = 11   **5.** 72 ÷ ☐ = 9   **6.** 35 ÷ ☐ = 5

Name _____ Date _____

Hands On: Model Fractions

CA Standards
NS 1.5, NS 1.7

Write a fraction for the shaded part. Then write a fraction for the part that is not shaded.

1.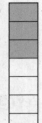

2.

3.

4.

_____   _____   _____   _____

On a separate piece of paper, draw a picture to show each fraction.

5. $\frac{4}{6}$ 6. $\frac{2}{5}$ 7. $\frac{7}{8}$ 8. $\frac{6}{7}$ 9. $\frac{2}{9}$ 10. $\frac{3}{10}$

Match the picture to the description. Write A or B.

A   B

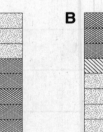

11. $\frac{3}{8}$ is [▨]

12. $\frac{6}{8}$ both [░] and [▨]

_____   _____

13. $\frac{1}{8}$ is [▨]

14. $\frac{8}{8}$ is NOT [▨]

_____   _____

Test Practice

Circle the letter of the correct answer.

15. Jessica goes to school for 5 days out of each week. What fraction of each week (7 days) does she NOT go to school?

A $\frac{5}{7}$ C $\frac{1}{7}$

B $\frac{2}{7}$ D $\frac{7}{7}$

16. Katie has 4 pets. Two of her pets are dogs. What fraction of her pets are dogs?

A $\frac{1}{8}$ C $\frac{1}{4}$

B $\frac{2}{4}$ D $\frac{3}{4}$

Writing Math There are 3 blue marbles, 7 green marbles, and 5 swirled marbles in a circle. What fraction of the marbles are blue?

Fractional Parts of a Number

Problem of the Day ———————————————————— NS 1.5

Hannah draws 8 shapes. $\frac{3}{8}$ of the shapes are circles. Use counters to model this fraction. How many of the shapes Hannah draws are circles?

Number Sense ———————————————————— KEY NS 3.0

Convert.

1. 17 m = ____ cm

2. 5,000 L = ____ KL

3. 300 dm = ____ cm

4. 4 Kg = ____ g

Word of the Day ———————————————————— NS 1.5

fractional

What word do you notice is part of fractional? When the suffix -al is added to the end of a word it changes the word from a noun to an adjective. The word fraction is a noun. The word fractional is an adjective that describes the part of the whole.

_____

_____

_____

Facts Practice ———————————————————— KEY NS 3.0

Divide.

1. $874 \div 4$ **2.** $943 \div 6$ **3.** $1,672 \div 8$

4. $4,591 \div 4$ **5.** $9,321 \div 5$ **6.** $4,602 \div 7$

Name _____   Date _____

Fractional Parts of a Number

CA Standard
NS 1.5

Find the fractional part of each number.

1. $\frac{2}{3}$ of 9

_____

2. $\frac{1}{6}$ of 12

_____

3. $\frac{1}{3}$ of 15

_____

4. $\frac{2}{3}$ of 18

_____

5. $\frac{1}{10}$ of 30

_____

6. $\frac{3}{4}$ of 8

_____

7. $\frac{2}{7}$ of 21

_____

8. $\frac{4}{5}$ of 25

_____

9. $\frac{5}{12}$ of 24

_____

10. $\frac{5}{7}$ of 14

_____

11. $\frac{8}{9}$ of 18

_____

12. $\frac{1}{3}$ of 6

_____

13. $\frac{5}{8}$ of 16

_____

14. $\frac{7}{10}$ of 30

_____

15. $\frac{5}{6}$ of 24

_____

16. $\frac{9}{10}$ of 50

_____

 **Test Practice**

Circle the letter of the correct answer.

17. Lucy is $\frac{1}{5}$ as old as her grandmother, Dorothy. If Dorothy is 60 years old, how old is Lucy?

   A 6   **C** 15

   B 5   **D** 12

18. Evan has 24 pairs of socks. If $\frac{1}{3}$ of the socks are blue, how many socks are not blue?

   A 0   **C** 8

   B 16   **D** 24

Writing Math Jake has 28 trading cards. Three fourths of the cards are baseball cards. How many of the cards are baseball cards?

_____

Hands On: Model Equivalent Fractions

Problem of the Day ———————————————————— NS 1.5

Connor swims 20 laps during swim practice. He swims $\frac{3}{5}$ of the laps using the backstroke. How many laps did Conner swim using the backstroke?

Number Sense ———————————————————————— AF 1.0

Use properties and rules to solve. List the property you used.

1. $3 \times$ ____ $= 0$

2. $17 \times 5 =$ ____ $\times 17$

3. $(8 \times 2) \times 2 = 8 \times (2 \times$ ____ $)$

4. $150 \times$ ____ $= 150$

Word of the Day ———————————————————————— NS 1.5

equivalent

Equivalent means *equal to.* What are some other words that mean equal?

_____

_____

_____

Facts Practice ——————————————————————— KEY NS 3.0

Multiply.

1. 50×20

2. 10×30

3. 200×80

4. 500×30

5. 700×500

6. $1,000 \times 600$

Name _____ Date _____

Hands On: Model Equivalent Fractions

CA Standards
NS 1.7, KEY NS 1.9

**Decide whether the fractional parts are equivalent. Write yes or no.
Use fraction strips to help you.**

1. $\frac{2}{6}$ and $\frac{1}{3}$

2. $\frac{5}{6}$ and $\frac{2}{3}$

3. $\frac{3}{5}$ and $\frac{6}{10}$

4. $\frac{1}{4}$ and $\frac{3}{10}$

_____

_____

_____

_____

5. $\frac{3}{12}$ and $\frac{2}{8}$

6. $\frac{10}{12}$ and $\frac{5}{6}$

7. $\frac{3}{4}$ and $\frac{9}{12}$

8. $\frac{7}{8}$ and $\frac{11}{12}$

_____

_____

_____

_____

**Find a fraction equivalent to each.
Draw number lines to help you.**

9. $\frac{4}{6}$

10. $\frac{2}{5}$

11. $\frac{6}{8}$

12. $\frac{5}{6}$

13. $\frac{3}{9}$

14. $\frac{4}{10}$

_____ _____ _____ _____ _____ _____

Test Practice

Circle the letter of the correct answer.

15. Matt split a circle into 3 equal parts and shaded 1 part. Mary split a congruent circle into 12 equal parts. How many parts should Mary shade in so that her circle shows a fraction that is equivalent to Matt's?

   A 4 parts   C 6 parts

   B 3 parts   D 2 parts

16. Alex ate 4 slices from a pie with 10 slices. Which fraction represents the portion of the pie he did not eat?

   A $\frac{2}{5}$ C $\frac{4}{10}$

   B $\frac{3}{5}$ D $\frac{6}{8}$

Writing Math Lars split a rectangle into 8 equal parts and shaded 6 parts. Mick split a congruent rectangle into 12 equal parts and shaded 8 parts. Do the two rectangles show equivalent fractions?

_____

Use with text pp. 374–375

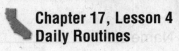
Equivalent Fractions

Problem of the Day ———————————————— NS 1.7

Emmanuel used a fraction circle to represent $\frac{1}{8}$. He said that $\frac{2}{4}$ is the same as $\frac{1}{8}$. Is he correct? Why or why not?

Algebra and Functions ———————————————— AF 1.0

Use *n* to write an algebraic expression for each word phrase.

1. the difference between a number and 8

2. a number times 9

3. the sum of 12 and a number

4. a number divided by 7

Number of the Day ———————————————— NS 1.5

$\frac{2}{7}$

This fraction represents the number of days of the week that is considered weekend days. What fraction of the week is considered work days?

_____

_____

_____

Facts Practice ———————————————— KEY NS 3.2

Divide.

1. $300 \div 30$

2. $7{,}000 \div 7$

3. $800 \div 100$

4. $5{,}000 \div 50$

Equivalent Fractions

CA Standards
NS 1.5, **KEY** NS 1.9

**Are the fractions in each pair equivalent?
Explain how you know.**

1. $\frac{4}{6}$ and $\frac{12}{18}$ 2. $\frac{3}{8}$ and $\frac{7}{16}$ 3. $\frac{2}{5}$ and $\frac{5}{10}$ 4. $\frac{3}{7}$ and $\frac{6}{14}$

_____   _____   _____   _____

Write each fraction in simplest form. Then write another equivalent fraction.

5. $\frac{4}{8}$ 6. $\frac{2}{6}$ 7. $\frac{8}{10}$ 8. $\frac{8}{12}$ 9. $\frac{5}{10}$

_____   _____   _____   _____   _____

10. $\frac{14}{16}$ 11. $\frac{9}{15}$ 12. $\frac{15}{20}$ 13. $\frac{8}{24}$ 14. $\frac{3}{12}$

_____   _____   _____   _____   _____

Find the value of x.

15. $\frac{X}{80} = \frac{1}{4}$ 16. $\frac{3}{9} = \frac{X}{3}$ 17. $\frac{9}{12} = \frac{X}{4}$ 18. $\frac{3}{5} = \frac{X}{10}$ 19. $\frac{10}{X} = \frac{5}{6}$

_____   _____   _____   _____   _____

Test Practice

Circle the letter of the correct answer.

20. Which fraction shows $\frac{9}{24}$ in simplest form?

    A $\frac{18}{48}$ C $\frac{1}{6}$

    B $\frac{3}{8}$ D $\frac{2}{7}$

21. Which fraction is not equivalent to $\frac{1}{3}$?

    A $\frac{2}{6}$ C $\frac{3}{9}$

    B $\frac{4}{10}$ D $\frac{5}{15}$

 **Writing Math** Kelly's softball team played 24 games and won 18 of them. Write the portion of games her team won as a fraction in simplest form.

Name _____ Date _____

Add and Subtract Fractions

Problem of the Day ———————————————————————— NS 1.5

Find two different fractions that are each equivalent to $\frac{2}{6}$.

Number Sense ——————————————————————————— KEY NS 3.0

Round each number to the nearest hundred or thousand. Then multiply.

1. 785×138

2. 212×553

3. $7,782 \times 284$

4. $4,902 \times 3,781$

Number of the Day ————————————————————————— NS 1.5

1

Sometimes a fraction has the same numerator and denominator. This fraction is equal to 1.

_____

_____

_____

Facts Practice ——————————————————————————— KEY NS 1.2

Compare. Write >, <, or = for each ◯.

1. 73,881 ◯ 78,331   2. 52,106 ◯ 52,601   3. 133,671 ◯ 132,671

4. 129,317 ◯ 129,318   5. 1,218,662 ◯ 1,218,226   6. 13,892,428 ◯ 23,892,428

Add and Subtract Fractions

CA Standards
NS 1.5, NS 1.7

Add or subtract.

1.
| 1 |
| $\frac{1}{4}$ | $\frac{1}{4}$ | $\frac{1}{4}$ | |

$\frac{2}{4} + \frac{1}{4} =$ _____

2.
| 1 |
| $\frac{1}{7}$ | $\frac{1}{7}$ | $\frac{1}{7}$ | | | | |

$\frac{3}{7} - \frac{2}{7} =$ _____

3.
| 1 |
| $\frac{1}{5}$ | $\frac{1}{5}$ | $\frac{1}{5}$ | $\frac{1}{5}$ | $\frac{1}{5}$ |

$\frac{1}{5} + \frac{4}{5} =$ _____

4. $\frac{1}{8} + \frac{1}{8} =$ _____

5. $\frac{2}{5} + \frac{2}{5} =$ _____

6. $\frac{4}{10} + \frac{3}{10} =$ _____

7. $\frac{2}{9} + \frac{7}{9} =$ _____

8. $\frac{5}{7} + \frac{1}{7} =$ _____

Algebra Variables • Find the value of *n*.

9. $\frac{7}{8} - \frac{n}{8} = \frac{2}{8}$ _____

10. $\frac{n}{12} + \frac{5}{12} = \frac{9}{12}$ _____

11. $\frac{9}{9} - \frac{n}{9} = \frac{4}{9}$ _____

Test Practice

Circle the letter of the correct answer.

12. Which fraction shows the sum of $\frac{3}{9}$ and $\frac{2}{9}$?

A $\frac{5}{9}$ C $\frac{2}{9}$

B $\frac{1}{9}$ D $\frac{9}{9}$

13. Which fraction shows the difference $\frac{3}{5} - \frac{2}{5}$?

A $\frac{1}{5}$ C $\frac{2}{5}$

B $\frac{3}{5}$ D $\frac{5}{5}$

Writing Math Mary separates an orange into 8 equal sections. She eats 3 sections and gives another 3 sections to her friend. What fraction shows how much of the orange is left over?

Problem Solving: Use a Simpler Problem

Problem of the Day ———————————————————— NS 1.5

The pizza Carlton's family ordered was cut into 8 equal sized pieces. Carlton ate 2 slices of pizza. His sister ate 1 slice of pizza. What fraction of the pizza did Carlton and his sister eat altogether?

Number Sense ———————————————————— KEY NS 3.0

Find the missing number.

1. $58 \div$ ____ $= 11$ R8

2. $23 \div$ ____ $= 2$ R3

3. $78 \div$ ____ $= 8$ R6

4. $50 \div$ ____ $= 7$ R1

Word of the Day ———————————————————— KEY NS 3.0

operation

In mathematics an *operation* is something that is being performed on a set of numbers. What are the four major operations?

_____

_____

_____

Facts Practice ———————————————————— KEY AF 1.2

Simplify.

1. $13 - (8 \times 2 \div 2)$

2. $15 \times 3 - (45 \div 5)$

3. $(28 + 2) + (15 \div 3)$

4. $17 + (20 \div 5) \div 2$

5. $18 + 5 - (3 + 2)$

6. $16 \div (6 + 1 + 1)$

Name _____ Date _____

Problem Solving:
Use a Simpler Problem

CA Standards
MR 2.2, NS 1.5

Use a simpler problem to solve.

1. Harry paid $\frac{5}{12}$ the price of a TV in January and the remainder in February. What

   fraction of the price did he pay in February? _____

2. Mindy ate $\frac{7}{16}$ of a bag of popcorn before the movie and $\frac{7}{16}$ during the movie. What

   fraction of the bag of popcorn was leftover? _____

3. Ben has $\frac{7}{12}$ of a pound of candy and Liana has $\frac{5}{12}$ of a pound. How much more

   candy does Ben have? _____

4. Markus rode his bike $\frac{7}{12}$ of the distance from his house to his friend
   Matt's house. What fraction of the distance does he still need to ride?

   _____

Test Practice

Circle the letter of the correct answer.

5. Alex has $\frac{2}{17}$ of a full basket of apples.
   Bettina has $\frac{8}{17}$ of a full basket. What
   fraction of a basket will they have if
   they combine their apples?

   A $\frac{2}{17}$ **C** $\frac{6}{17}$

   B $\frac{8}{17}$ **D** $\frac{10}{17}$

6. Maribel and Johnny are comparing
   their notebooks. Maribel's notebook
   is $\frac{5}{6}$ filled and Johnny's notebook
   is $\frac{1}{6}$ filled. How much more filled is
   Maribel's notebook?

   A $\frac{1}{6}$ **C** $\frac{4}{6}$

   B $\frac{5}{6}$ **D** $\frac{6}{6}$

Writing Math Mr. Ho is at the supermarket. He wants to
find the total number of pounds of cherries in three bags. The bags
weigh $\frac{1}{8}$ pounds, $\frac{3}{8}$ pounds, and $\frac{2}{8}$ pounds respectively. Explain how
Mr. Ho can find the total weight of the bags of cherries. What is the
total weight?

_____

Hands On: Compare Fractions

Problem of the Day ————————————————————— KEY NS 3.2

How many grams are 6 kilograms?

Number Sense Review ————————————————————— KEY NS 1.8

Use Workmat 4 to plot these numbers on the number line.

−3, 4, 10, −9, 0

Word of the Day ————————————————————————— MR 2.3

compare

Think of everyday occurrences when you might compare things.

_____

_____

_____

Facts Practice ————————————————————————— KEY NS 1.8

Compare using >, <, or =.

1. −17 ____ −3

2. 15 ____ −20

3. 0 ____ −6

4. −2 ____ −5

5. −20 ____ 41

6. 31 ____ −10

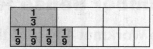
Hands On: Compare Fractions

Compare. Write >, <, or = for each ◯. Use fraction tiles or
number lines to help you.

1. $\frac{6}{10}$ ◯ $\frac{5}{10}$

| $\frac{1}{10}$ | $\frac{1}{10}$ | $\frac{1}{10}$ | $\frac{1}{10}$ | $\frac{1}{10}$ | $\frac{1}{10}$ | | |
| $\frac{1}{10}$ | $\frac{1}{10}$ | $\frac{1}{10}$ | $\frac{1}{10}$ | $\frac{1}{10}$ | | | |

2. $\frac{3}{4}$ ◯ $\frac{6}{8}$

| $\frac{1}{4}$ | $\frac{1}{4}$ | $\frac{1}{4}$ | |
| $\frac{1}{8}$ | $\frac{1}{8}$ | $\frac{1}{8}$ | $\frac{1}{8}$ | $\frac{1}{8}$ | $\frac{1}{8}$ | |

3. $\frac{1}{3}$ ◯ $\frac{4}{9}$

| $\frac{1}{3}$ | | |
| $\frac{1}{9}$ | $\frac{1}{9}$ | $\frac{1}{9}$ | $\frac{1}{9}$ | | | |

4. $\frac{6}{12}$ ◯ $\frac{3}{6}$ _____

5. $\frac{1}{6}$ ◯ $\frac{3}{12}$ _____

6. $\frac{4}{12}$ ◯ $\frac{3}{6}$ _____

7. $\frac{1}{5}$ ◯ $\frac{3}{15}$ _____

8. $\frac{8}{9}$ ◯ $\frac{7}{8}$ _____

9. $\frac{2}{4}$ ◯ $\frac{6}{12}$ _____

10. $\frac{3}{4}$ ◯ $\frac{4}{5}$ _____

11. $\frac{8}{9}$ ◯ $\frac{6}{9}$ _____

 Test Practice

Circle the letter of the correct answer.

12. Andy drew a line that was $\frac{7}{8}$ of an inch long. Ally drew a line that was $\frac{11}{36}$ of an inch
long. Akim drew a line that was $\frac{3}{4}$ of an inch long. Which person's line, if any, was
longest?

A Andy's line

c Ally's line

B Akim's line

D They were all equal.

13. Fred split a square into 4 equal smaller squares and shaded 2 of the squares. Frank
split a square into 8 equal rectangles and shaded 6 of the rectangles. Francine split a
square into 6 equal rectangles and shaded 3 of the rectangles. Which person, if any,
shaded in a larger fraction of his or her square?

A Fred

c Francine

B Frank

D They were all equal.

Writing Math Maggie changed all the denominators in problem 12 to 36, but left
the numerators the same. She said that Ally's line was now the longest. Is she right? Explain.

_____

_____

Compare and Order Fractions

Problem of the Day ————————————————— KEY NS 1.9

Sophie has eaten $\frac{1}{2}$ of her pizza. Model this fraction on a number line.

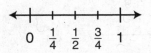

Number Sense Review ————————————————— KEY NS 3.0

Find the other multiplication fact and two division facts that make up the fact family.

1. $6 \times 7 = 42$

2. $3 \times 4 = 12$

3. $7 \times 8 = 56$

Word of the Day ————————————————— KEY NS 4.2

prime

Give five examples of prime numbers.

_____

_____

_____

Facts Practice ————————————————— KEY NS 3.2

Multiply or divide.

1. $121 \div 11$ **2.** 11×11 **3.** 10×10

4. $100 \div 10$ **5.** $16 \div 4$ **6.** 4×4

Compare and Order Fractions

CA Standards
KEY NS 1.9, NS 1.5

Compare. Write >, <, or = for each ◯.

1. $\frac{6}{10}$ ◯ $\frac{3}{10}$ _____

2. $\frac{3}{4}$ ◯ $\frac{6}{8}$ _____

3. $\frac{1}{3}$ ◯ $\frac{6}{9}$ _____

4. $\frac{6}{12}$ ◯ $\frac{2}{4}$ _____

5. $\frac{1}{6}$ ◯ $\frac{3}{9}$ _____

6. $\frac{1}{12}$ ◯ $\frac{3}{6}$ _____

7. $\frac{1}{5}$ ◯ $\frac{3}{15}$ _____

8. $\frac{8}{9}$ ◯ $\frac{5}{6}$ _____

9. $\frac{3}{6}$ ◯ $\frac{6}{12}$ _____

10. $\frac{4}{4}$ ◯ $\frac{5}{6}$ _____

11. $\frac{8}{9}$ ◯ $\frac{9}{9}$ _____

Order the fractions from least to greatest. Use number lines to help you.

12. $\frac{1}{4}$ $\frac{3}{4}$ $\frac{2}{4}$

13. $\frac{2}{7}$ $\frac{6}{7}$ $\frac{4}{7}$

14. $\frac{7}{9}$ $\frac{3}{9}$ $\frac{5}{9}$

15. $\frac{5}{8}$ $\frac{3}{8}$ $\frac{1}{4}$

_____ _____ _____ _____

Test Practice

Circle the letter of the correct answer.

16. Which set of fractions is ordered from greatest to least?

A $\frac{2}{3}, \frac{1}{2}, \frac{3}{5}$

C $\frac{2}{5}, \frac{3}{5}, \frac{4}{5}$

B $\frac{3}{4}, \frac{3}{5}, \frac{3}{6}$

D $\frac{1}{3}, \frac{1}{5}, \frac{1}{4}$

17. Ted drew a line that was $\frac{2}{6}$ of an inch long. Toni drew a line that was $\frac{11}{36}$ of an inch long. Tara drew a line that was $\frac{1}{6}$ of an inch long. Which person's line, if any, was longer?

A Tara's line   C Toni's line

B Ted's line   D They were all equal.

Writing Math In problem 16 above, which was the easiest set of fractions to order? Which was the hardest? Explain.

_____

_____

_____

Write Mixed Numbers and Improper Fractions

Problem of the Day ———————————————— KEY NS 1.9

Tenecia ate $\frac{3}{8}$ of a box of raisins and her cousin Beau ate $\frac{5}{16}$ of a box of raisins. Who ate more raisins?

Number Sense Review ———————————————— KEY NS 1.8

Use Workmat 4 to order the numbers −2, 1, −6, −3, and 5 and list them from least to greatest.

Number of the Day ———————————————— KEY NS 4.2

6

The number 6 is called a perfect number because the sum of its factors (other than itself) is the number. Can you find another perfect number under 30?

_____

_____

_____

Facts Practice ———————————————— KEY AF 2.0

Solve each equation.

1. $4r = 16$

2. $56 = 8p$

3. $\frac{b}{3} = 12$

4. $9 = \frac{w}{6}$

5. $11t = 55$

6. $\frac{s}{4} = 15$

Name _____ Date _____

Write Mixed Numbers and Improper Fractions

CA Standards
KEY NS 1.9, NS 1.7

Write an improper fraction and a mixed number or whole number to describe the shaded parts.

1.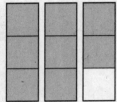

2.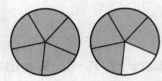

3.

_____ _____ _____

_____ _____ _____

Write a mixed number and an improper fraction for each letter.

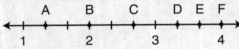

4. E   5. B   6. D   7. A   8. C   9. F

_____   _____   _____   _____   _____   _____

Test Practice

Circle the letter of the correct answer.

10. Which improper fraction is equivalent to $3\frac{3}{8}$?

A $\frac{27}{3}$ C $\frac{28}{8}$

B $\frac{27}{8}$ D $\frac{33}{8}$

11. Julie brought 3 pies to Thanksgiving dinner. Each pie was cut into 8 pieces. Each person ate 2 pieces, and there were no pieces left over. How many people were at the dinner?

A 10 people   C 12 people

B 14 people   D 16 people

Writing Math If one more section in problem 1 was shaded, would the answer be a mixed number or a whole number? Explain.

Compare and Order Fractions and Mixed Numbers

Problem of the Day

Natasha, Elena and Madison are running a race. After 20 minutes, Madison has run 0.9 miles, Natasha has run 2.1 miles, and Elena has run 1.8 miles. Order the runners from fastest to slowest.

Number Sense Review

Tell how many meters.

1. 3 kilometers

2. 400 decimeters

3. 200 centimeters

Number of the Day

$\frac{1}{4}$

How many fourths make up one whole?

_____

_____

_____

Facts Practice

Estimate to find the products or quotients.

1. 83×4 2. 690×21 3. 520×33

4. $82 \div 9$ 5. $50 \div 7$ 6. $145 \div 12$

Compare and Order Fractions and Mixed Numbers

CA Standards
KEY NS 1.9, NS 1.5

Compare. Write >, <, or = for each ◯.

1. $2\frac{3}{5}$ ◯ $2\frac{4}{10}$ _____

2. $1\frac{2}{6}$ ◯ $\frac{4}{3}$ _____

3. $1\frac{3}{4}$ ◯ $1\frac{7}{8}$ _____

4. $3\frac{3}{9}$ ◯ $\frac{13}{3}$ _____

Order the numbers from least to greatest. Use number lines to help you.

5. $2\frac{5}{8}$ $1\frac{4}{8}$ $2\frac{2}{4}$ _____

6. $6\frac{1}{3}$ $\frac{61}{9}$ $6\frac{6}{9}$ _____

7. $1\frac{8}{10}$ $1\frac{3}{5}$ $1\frac{7}{10}$ _____

8. $\frac{32}{6}$ $5\frac{2}{3}$ $5\frac{1}{6}$ _____

Test Practice

Circle the letter of the correct answer.

9. Which number is the greatest?

A $1\frac{3}{15}$ C $1\frac{4}{5}$

B $\frac{11}{5}$ D $1\frac{1}{3}$

10. Which number is the least?

A $2\frac{3}{4}$ C $2\frac{4}{16}$

B $\frac{10}{4}$ D $2\frac{4}{8}$

Writing Math Jon was ordering fractions in which the denominators were 2, 3, and 4. He said he couldn't do it because there was no common denominator for these three numbers. Is he correct? Explain.

_____

_____

Problem Solving: Field Trip

Problem of the Day ─────────────────────────── KEY NS 1.9

On Monday, Patrick ran $3\frac{3}{4}$ miles. On Wednesday he ran $2\frac{7}{8}$ miles, and on Friday he ran $3\frac{15}{16}$ miles. On which day did Patrick run the farthest?

Number Sense Review ───────────────────────── KEY NS 3.0

Write an example of the Commutative Property of Multiplication.

Word of the Day ─────────────────────────────── MR 2.3

function rule

Can you find a *function rule* if you only know one input and one output value?

_____

_____

_____

Facts Practice ──────────────────────────────── KEY NS 3.2

Find the missing number.

1. 500 cm = _____ m

2. _____ mm = 7 m

3. 30 dm = _____ cm

4. 4 km = _____ m

5. _____ cm = 9,000 mm

6. _____ km = 100,000 cm

181

Hands On: Fractions and Decimals

Problem of the Day

Benjamin is making toffee with his mom. They make a pan and cut it into six separate parts. If he eats $\frac{1}{6}$ of one of the pan, what fraction of the toffee will they have left over to give away?

Number Sense Review

Use Workmat 2 to write the following number in standard form.

thirty-seven thousand, ten

Word of the Day

million

Throughout the day, see how often you encounter or hear "million."

_____

_____

_____

Facts Practice

Add or subtract. Put your answer in simplest form.

1. $\frac{1}{5} + \frac{3}{5}$

2. $\frac{1}{9} + \frac{2}{9}$

3. $\frac{4}{5} + \frac{1}{5}$

4. $\frac{6}{11} - \frac{3}{11}$

5. $\frac{7}{8} - \frac{3}{8}$

6. $\frac{9}{13} - \frac{6}{13}$

Name _____ Date _____

Hands On: Fractions and Decimals

Use grid paper to show the following fractions and decimals.

1. 0.9

2. $\frac{80}{100}$

3. 0.31

4. $\frac{8}{100}$

5. 0.4

6. $\frac{8}{10}$

Test Practice

Circle the letter of the correct answer.

7. Which of the following numbers names the shaded part of the grid?

  A 6   **C** 0.6

  B $\frac{6}{100}$ **D** $\frac{10}{6}$

8. Which of the following numbers names the shaded part of the grid?

  A 0.07   **C** 0.77

  B $\frac{70}{100}$ **D** $\frac{70}{1000}$

 Writing Math How would you explain the difference between

0.17 and $\frac{18}{100}$?

_____

_____

_____

_____

_____

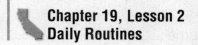
Mixed Numbers and Decimals

Problem of the Day ——————————————————— NS 1.6

Which base-ten blocks should Maria use to model the decimal 1.69?

Algebra and Functions Review ———————————— KEY AF 1.3

Place parentheses in the expression so that the value is equal
to 20.

$2 \times 5 + 5$

Number of the Day ——————————————————— NS 1.6

6.91

What number is in the tenths place?

_____

_____

_____

Facts Practice ——————————————————————— KEY NS 3.2

Multiply.

1. 8×9 **2.** 4×11 **3.** 7×5

4. 6×12 **5.** 3×8

Mixed Numbers and Decimals

CA Standards
NS 1.0, NS 1.6

Write each as a decimal.

1. $3\frac{1}{10}$

_____

2. $47\frac{8}{100}$

_____

3. $2\frac{1}{10}$

_____

4. $6\frac{8}{100}$

_____

5. $5\frac{99}{100}$

_____

6. seven and
four tenths

_____

7. eighty-two
hundredths

_____

8. six and
ninety-nine
hundredths

_____

Test Practice

9. Amy opened 3 boxes of holiday
ornaments. Each box contained 100
ornaments. One box of ornaments plus
23 of the ornaments in another box
were broken. Which decimal represents
the number of boxes with broken
ornaments?

   A 12.3   C 1.23

   B 1.023   D 0.123

10. Ginny is loading a photocopier with
paper. Each package of blank paper
contains 100 sheets. Ginny tries to
place a whole package in the copier,
but the paper drawer won't close. After
she removes 30 sheets, the drawer
closes easily. Which decimal represents
the number of packages of paper that
Ginny added to the copier?

    A 1.7   C 0.3

    B 0.70   D 1.3

 Writing Math Write 3.62 in word form.

_____

Name _____ Date _____

Fractions and Decimal Equivalents

Problem of the Day ———————————————————— NS 1.6

Each day Briana walks one and three tenths miles to school. How can this distance be written as a mixed number and a decimal?

Number Sense Review ———————————————— KEY **NS 1.9**

Write 2 fractions which are less than $\frac{3}{4}$ and 2 which are greater than $\frac{3}{4}$.

Word of the Day ———————————————————————— NS 1.0

tenth

What are some items that are divided into tenths or shown as tenths?

_____

_____

_____

Facts Practice ———————————————————————— NS 1.5

Find each sum or difference.

1. $\frac{7}{8} - \frac{2}{8}$

2. $\frac{3}{5} + \frac{2}{5}$

3. $\frac{3}{4} - \frac{1}{4}$

4. $\frac{4}{10} - \frac{3}{10}$

5. $\frac{2}{9} + \frac{2}{9}$

6. $\frac{1}{6} + \frac{4}{6}$

Fractions and Decimal Equivalents

CA Standards
NS 1.6, NS 1.7

Write a fraction and a decimal to describe the shaded part of each.

1.

2.

3.

4.

_____   _____   _____   _____

Write each decimal as an equivalent fraction. Write each fraction as an equivalent decimal.

5. 0.20

6. 0.05

7. $\frac{3}{20}$

8. $\frac{8}{25}$

_____   _____   _____   _____

Test Practice

9. Suppose there are 100 cows, and 60 of the cows are spotted. If the rest are brown, how many cows are brown?

   A 40   **c** 60

   B 30   **D** 35

10. The floor of a kitchen is made of 100 square tiles. Most of the tiles are white, but 12 are red. Which decimal correctly identifies the part of all the tiles that are red?

   A 12   **c** 1.20

   B 0.12   **D** 120

Writing Math Explain how you would find the decimal equivalent for $\frac{1}{5}$.

_____

_____

Compare and Order Decimals

Problem of the Day ————————————————————

Ayame's scores at her gymnastics meet were 9.91, 9.72, and 10.0. Put these points on the number line.

Number Sense Review ————————————————

Multiply. Find a division sentence from the same fact family.

1. 6×7

2. 5×6

3. 11×10

Number of the Day ————————————————————

4.52

What are some other ways to write 4.52?

_____

_____

_____

Facts Practice ————————————————————————

Add or subtract.

1. $12 + 12$ **2.** $12 + 11$ **3.** $11 - 5$

4. $8 + 9$ **5.** $18 - 9$ **6.** $3 + 9$

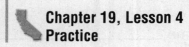
Compare and Order Decimals

CA Standards
KEY NS 1.2, **KEY** NS 1.9

Compare. Write >, <, or = for each ◯.

1. 5.01 ◯ 4.99   **2.** 18.5 ◯ 20.2   **3.** 12.47 ◯ 12.74   **4.** 9.56 ◯ 9.65

_____   _____   _____   _____

Order the numbers from least to greatest.

5. 3.13   3.33   3.83   3.31   **6.** 6.56   5.65   55.5   56.56

_____   _____

✓ Test Practice

Circle the letter of the correct answer.

7. Which of the following is the least number?

   A 0.03   **C** 0.31

   B 0.30   **D** 0.13

8. Which of the following is the greatest number?

   A 0.87   **C** 0.78

   B 0.83   **D** 0.09

Writing Math How would you write the decimal in the correct answer to problem 7 in words?

_____

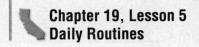
Compare and Order Fractions and Decimals

Problem of the Day ——————————————————— NS 1.0

Order the fractions from greatest to least.

$\frac{1}{4}$, $\frac{5}{8}$, $\frac{6}{8}$

Number Sense Review ——————————————— KEY

Write how many cups.

1. 2 pints

2. 1 gallon

3. 2 quarts

Number of the Day ——————————————————— KEY

4,208

Write the place value of each digit in the number 4,208.

_____

_____

_____

Facts Practice ——————————————————————— MR 2.3

Use patterns to multiply.

1. 6 × 10   **2.** 40 × 100

3. 23 × 10   **4.** 789 × 100

Compare and Order Fractions and Decimals

CA Standards
KEY NS 1.2, KEY NS 1.9

Compare. Write >, <, or = for each ⬭.

1. $3.03 \bigcirc 3\frac{3}{10}$

2. $2\frac{34}{100} \bigcirc 2.34$

3. $6.26 \bigcirc 6\frac{1}{4}$

Order the numbers from greatest to least.

4. $4.01 \quad 4\frac{2}{5} \quad 4\frac{8}{100} \quad 4.1$ _____

5. $2\frac{1}{2} \quad 3.1 \quad 2\frac{3}{10} \quad 3.04$

6. $1.1 \quad 1\frac{1}{100} \quad 1.001 \quad 10.1$

_____

_____

Test Practice

Circle the letter of the correct answer.

7. Which of the following is the least number?

A 4.31   C $4\frac{3}{10}$

B 4.36   D $4\frac{37}{100}$

8. Which of the following is the greatest number?

A $8\frac{12}{100}$ C 8.012

B $8\frac{2}{10}$ D 8.21

Writing Math How would you explain the difference between 2 tens and 2 tenths?

_____

_____

_____

_____

Problem Solving: Field Trip

Problem of the Day

Tyrone, James and Lita are on the school running team. On Monday, Tyrone ran 1.6 miles, James ran $\frac{6}{4}$ miles and Lita ran $1\frac{3}{4}$ miles? Who ran the greatest distance? Who ran the least distance?

Algebra and Functions Review

Write a word problem which could be represented by the equation shown below. Then solve for *x*.

$$\frac{42}{x} = 6$$

Number of the Day

0.1

How many tenths are in 1? How many tenths are in 100? How many tenths are in 1,000,000?

_____

_____

_____

Facts Practice

Write an equivalent fraction.

1. $\frac{2}{3}$ 2. $\frac{4}{12}$

4. $\frac{3}{10}$ 5. $\frac{2}{8}$

Hands On: Explore Addition and Subtraction of Decimals

Problem of the Day ——————————————— NS 1.6

Three of the students in Mrs. Lee's class have birthdays in the summer. Eight have birthdays in the fall, four in the winter and five in the spring. What fraction of the students have birthdays in the fall? How can this be written as a decimal?

Algebra and Functions ——————————— KEY AF 1.3

Use parentheses to write an expression in which the answer to the equation is 4.

Number of the Day ——————————————— NS 1.5

6

What does 6 represent when it is the numerator of a fraction? What does it represent when it is the denominator of a fraction?

_____

_____

_____

Facts Practice ——————————————————— KEY NS 1.8

Write the opposite of each number.

1. 6   2. ⁻12   3. 7

4. ⁻4   5. ⁻3   6. 9

Name _____ Date _____

Hands On: Explore Addition and Subtraction of Decimals

CA Standards
NS 2.0, NS 2.1

Find the sum or difference. Use models if you wish.

1. $1.8 - 0.2$

2. $0.6 + 0.5$

3. $1.6 - 0.7$

4. $1.5 + 0.3$

_____

_____

_____

_____

5. $1.8 + 2.3$

6. $3.2 + 6.9$

7. $2.3 + 3.7$

8. $5.2 - 3.8$

_____

_____

_____

_____

9. $2.63 - 1.54$

10. $1.09 + 2.13$

11. $4.16 - 2.08$

12. $3.45 + 4.87$

_____

_____

_____

_____

Test Practice

Circle the letter of the correct answer.

13. John does a standing long jump that is 1.57 meters. Jerry does a standing long jump that is 1.74 meters. How much longer is Jerry's jump?

   A 0.17 meters   **C** 3.31 meters

   B 1.17 meters   **D** 0.31 meters

14. Georgia is mixing paints together. She mixes 0.53 quarts of red paint with 0.37 quarts of yellow paint. How many quarts of mixed paint does she get?

   A 0.09 quarts   **C** 0.9 quarts

   B 9 quarts   **D** 90 quarts

Writing Math Nan says that 1.70 is the same as 1.7. Do you agree? Explain your answer.

_____

_____

_____

Use with text pp. 440–441

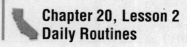
Round Decimals

Problem of the Day ———————————————————————— NS 2.1

Charley bought a notebook for $2.45 and a pencil for $0.75. How much did the notebook and pencil cost altogether? How much change did Charley get if he gave the clerk $3.50?

Number Sense ——————————————————————————————— NS 1.0

Write the decimal 1.45 three different ways.

Word of the Day ————————————————————————————— MR 3.0

deci-

What words can you think of that start with dec- or deci-? What do these words have in common?

_____

_____

_____

Facts Practice ——————————————————————————————— NS 1.6

Write each as a fraction.

1. 2.3   **2.** 4.34   **3.** 6.09

4. 3.72   **5.** 5.03   **6.** 19.98

Name _____ Date _____

Round Decimals

CA Standards
NS 2.2, MR 2.5

Round each decimal to the nearest whole number.

1. 32.87 _____

2. 9.481 _____

3. 57.224 _____

4. 5.247 _____

5. 351.58 _____

6. 865.12 _____

7. 45.512 _____

8. 1.238 _____

9. 54.579 _____

10. 17.54 _____

11. 1,235.84 _____

12. 542.23 _____

13. 42.325 _____

14. 78.953 _____

15. 42.336 _____

Round each decimal to the place of the underlined digit.

16. 75.6 _____

17. 5.3 _____

18. 6.71 _____

19. 1,482.23 _____

20. 67.54 _____

21. 81.246 _____

22. 172.34 _____

23. 8.95 _____

24. 237.354 _____

25. 87.321 _____

26. 15.87 _____

27. 56.37 _____

28. 89.324 _____

29. 750.158 _____

30. 57.339 _____

 **Test Practice**

Circle the letter of the correct answer.

31. Aaron has 8.39 kg of apples. What is the weight of the apples to the nearest whole kilogram?

   A 8.3 kilograms   C 8 kilograms

   B 8.30 kilograms   D 9 kilograms

32. Julie lives $3\frac{1}{4}$ km from the market. What is this distance to the nearest tenth kilometer?

   A 3.0 kilometers   C 3.2 kilometers

   B 3.3 kilometers   D 3.5 kilometers

Writing Math Samuel bought 4.65 pounds of apples. He says he bought about 5 pounds. Do you agree? Explain your answer.

_____

_____

_____

Estimate Decimal Sums and Differences

Problem of the Day ———————————————— NS 2.2

Martina bought 4.53 pounds of beef. What is this rounded to the
nearest tenth? What is it rounded to the nearest pound?

Measurement and Geometry ———————————— MG 1.0

List the length and width of 3 rectangles with a perimeter of
22 inches.

Number of the Day ———————————————————— NS 4.0

54

List all the factors of the number 54.

_____

_____

_____

Facts Practice ——————————————————— KEY NS 3.2

Find the missing number.

1. 8 pt = ____ qt   **2.** 3 lb = ____ oz   **3.** 12 c = ____ qt

4. 5 gal = ____ pt   **5.** 6 T = ____ lb   **6.** 4 gal = ____ c

Estimate Decimal Sums and Differences

CA Standards
NS 2.1, NS 2.2

Estimate by rounding to the nearest whole number. Solve.

1. 9.3
   +6.1

2. 7.3
   −4.7

3. $83.82
   + 24.13

4. $45.38
   − 18.77

5. 38.872
   +25.913

6. $8.92
   − 4.23

7. 48.32
   +68.37

8. 73.253
   −45.892

9. $46.22
   + 89.79

10. 64.327
    −32.781

Estimate by rounding to the nearest $10 and to the nearest $100. Solve.

11. $832.34 + $243.98

12. $581.48 − $293.98

13. $184.33 + $284.79

14. $465.81 − $368.54

15. $346.55 + $784.15

16. $412.84 − $335.71

17. $584.35 + $953.51

18. $334.58 − $227.49

19. $848.84 − $484.48

Test Practice

Circle the letter of the correct answer.

20. Brian has 12 meters of canvas for his paintings. He uses 4.78 m for one painting and 5.87 m for another. About how much canvas does he have left?

   A 12 meters   C 1 meter

   B 2 meters   D 11 meters

21. Jeffrey is making a chair. He spent $14.87 on wood and $18.48 on other supplies. About how much did he spend in all?

   A $20.00   C $35.00

   B $33.00   D $40.00

Writing Math In an addition problem, if you round down both numbers how will the estimated sum compare with the exact answer?

_____

_____

Add and Subtract Decimals

Problem of the Day ——————————————————— NS 2.1

Nora has 4.37 yards of fencing and adds another 1.28 yards. How many yards of fencing does she have?

Algebraic Thinking ——————————————————— MR 1.1

Write the function rule.

Set A	Set B
13	30
23	40
33	50

Number of the Day ——————————————————— NS 1.0

4.09

Write the place value of each digit in the decimal.

_____

_____

_____

Facts Practice ——————————————————— KEY NS 3.1

Add or subtract.

1. 409.632 + 111,249

2. 8,023,647 − 124,500

3. 609,240 − 547,816

4. 762,431 + 567,928

Name _____ Date _____

Add and Subtract Decimals

CA Standards
NS 2.1, NS 2.2

Add or subtract. Use estimation to check.

1. 4.5
   +3.8

2. 4.8
   −2.5

3. $20.84
   + 15.35

4. $47.81
   − 39.19

5. 6.80
   +5.78

6. $35.46
   − 19.83

7. 6.841
   +8.304

8. 56.37
   −24.18

9. $89.21
   + 49.53

10. 8.245
    −6.176

Place the decimal points in the addends to make the sentences correct.

11. 84 + 42 = 12.6

12. 451 + 23 + 171 = 8.52

_____

_____

13. 017 + 087 + 381 = 4.85

14. 328 + 219 + 49 = 59.6

_____

_____

Test Practice

Circle the letter of the correct answer.

15. David drove 53.78 miles to his grandmother's house and then drove another 8.3 miles to his sister's house. How many miles did he drive in all?

   A 45.48 miles   **C** 546.1 miles

   B 62.08 miles   **D** 529.5 miles

16. Alan lives 2.48 kilometers from school. Warren lives 3.19 kilometers from school. How much farther from school does Warren live?

   A 0.071 kilometers   **C** 0.71 kilometers

   B 7.1 kilometers   **D** 71 kilometers

 Writing Math Explain how to add 4.5 to 7.26.

_____

_____

_____

_____

_____

Use with text pp. 448–451

Problem Solving: Work Backward

Problem of the Day ———————————————— KEY NS 1.2

Tao skates competitively. Her scores from her last competition were 9.5, 9.3 and 10.0. Write Tao's scores in order from least to greatest.

Number Sense ———————————————— KEY NS 3.2

Write how many pounds.

1. 3 tons

2. 320 ounces

3. 400 ounces

Word of the Day ———————————————— AF 1.1

variable

Write 3 expressions, equations, or inequalities with a variable.

_____

_____

_____

Facts Practice ———————————————— KEY NS 3.0

Multiply or divide.

1. $36 \div 6$

2. $32 \div 4$

3. $21 \div 7$

4. 7×7

5. 9×7

6. 9×4

Name _____ Date _____

Problem Solving: Work Backward

Work backward to solve each problem.

1. Niles is planning Orlando's surprise birthday party. He buys 8 bags of chips and 4 liters of lemonade. He spends $19.96. If each liter of lemonade costs $1.99, how much is the cost of each bag of chips?

   _____

2. Bernadette cuts a piece of wrapping paper in half, so she and her sister can wrap presents before they go to the party. Bernadette uses 1.3 yards of her half wrapping a present and still has 0.9 yards left. How long was the original piece of wrapping paper?

   _____

3. Orlando's mother is making the cake. She buys 3 pounds of flour, 1 dozen eggs, and a gallon of milk. The total cost is $8.99. If the milk cost $2.33 and the eggs cost $2.19, how much did she pay for 1 pound of flour?

   _____

Test Practice

Circle the letter of the correct answer.

4. Geoffrey has 24 DVDs. Half are Horror movies, 4 are Comedies, and the rest are Sci-Fi. How many DVDs are Sci-Fi?

   A 16   C 12

   B 10   D 8

5. Halley buys 2 bottles of shampoo, 4 bars of bath soap, and a bag of cotton balls. She pays $11.13. If each bar of soap cost 99¢ and the bag of cotton balls cost $1.99, how much was each bottle of shampoo?

   A $5.18   C $2.59

   B $1.96   D $1.09

Writing Math Wilson solved problem 5 above and got the answer $5.18. What did he do wrong?

_____

_____

Hands On: Plot Points

Problem of the Day ———————————————— NS 2.0

After Corinne got her allowance, she bought a new book for $5.34 and an art kit for $10.59. If Corinne has $4.07 left after her purchases, how much was her allowance?

Number Sense ———————————————— KEY NS 1.9

Order the fractions $\frac{5}{12}$, $\frac{3}{4}$, $\frac{2}{3}$, and $\frac{1}{2}$ from least to greatest.

Word of the Day ———————————————— MR 2.3

mixed number

Write some examples of *mixed numbers.* What two parts do these numbers contain?

_____

_____

_____

Facts Practice ———————————————— KEY AF 1.2

Copy and complete, using >, <, or =.

1. $(4 - 1) \times 3$ ____ 4×3

2. $4 + 6 \times 5$ ____ 10×5

3. $83 - 2$ ____ $(12 - 3) \times 9$

4. $(7 \times 3) + (20 - 8)$ ____ 32

5. $72 \div 8 \times 5$ ____ $(10 + 5) \times 3$

6. $144 \div (8 + 4)$ ____ 7×2

Name _____   Date _____

Hands On: Plot Points

CA Standards
KEY MG 2.0, MR 2.3

Use the graph on the right for Exercises 1–9. Write the letter of the point for each ordered pair.

1. (2, 6)   **2.** (3, 2)   **3.** (1, 4)

_____   _____   _____

Write the ordered pair for each point.

4. B   **5.** F   **6.** I

_____   _____   _____

7. Name the ordered pairs for *M, G,* and *F.* What do *M* and *F* have in common?

_____

8. Name three pairs of points where both points in the pair have the same first coordinate.

_____

9. Do point *M* and point *D* make a horizontal or vertical line segment?

_____

Test Practice

Circle the letter of the correct answer.

10. Which describes how to plot the point (3, 8)?

   A Start at 0, move 3 right, and then 8 up.

   B Start at 0, move 3 left, and then 8 up.

   C Start at 0, move 8 right, and then 3 up.

   D Start at 0, move 8 left, and then 3 down.

11. If you plot the points (1, 2) and (1, 5) and connect them, which must be true?

   A The points form a vertical line.

   B The points form a horizontal line.

   C The points do not form a vertical or horizontal line.

   D The points do not form a line.

Writing Math Write directions for locating a point whose coordinates are (4, 10).

_____

Plot and Name Points on a Grid

Problem of the Day — KEY MG 2.0

Describe how to plot the ordered pair (5, 2) on a grid.

Algebra and Functions — KEY AF 1.5

Write a function rule using two variables for the function table.

Input (x)	Output (y)
1	6
3	18
5	30

Number of the Day — KEY NS 1.8

−8

What number is the opposite of −8? How far apart are −8 and its opposite on the number line?

_____

_____

_____

Facts Practice — NS 2.2

Round each decimal to the nearest tenth and the nearest whole number.

1. 62.89   **2.** 109.61   **3.** 5.55

4. 2,438.32   **5.** 457.19   **6.** 9.54

Plot and Name Points on a Grid

CA Standards
KEY MG 2.0, MR 2.3

Plot each point and label it with the correct letter.

1. A (3, 5)
2. B (1, 6)
3. C (5, 6)
4. D (2, 4)
5. E (2, 0)
6. F (4, 2)
7. G (3, 1)
8. H (0, 4)
9. I (2, 6)
10. J (1, 5)

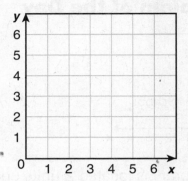

11. Sally collected snowfall data for an experiment. She wants to make a line graph of her data, which is shown below in the table. Plot and connect the points to make a line graph on the grid at the right.

Snowfall Data

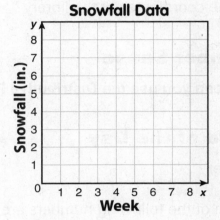

Snowfall Data								
Week	1	2	3	4	5	6	7	8
Snowfall (in.)	3	7	1	0	8	4	6	2

Test Practice

Circle the letter of the correct answer.

12. Suppose that you were to start at 0, then move 3 units to the right, then move 6 units up, and then make a dot. Which ordered pair matches the dot?

    A (6, 3)
    B (3, 6)
    C (0, 6)
    D (3, 0)

13. If point A (1, 4) is plotted on the same grid as point B (3, 7), which describes the location of the two points?

    A A is to the left of and up from B.
    B A is to the right of and up from B.
    C A is to the left of and down from B.
    D A is to the right of and down from B.

Writing Math Patrick plotted a point at (5, 4). He started at 0, moved up 5 units and then moved right 4 units. Explain what Patrick did wrong.

_____

_____

Use with text pp. 468–471

Graphs of Functions

Problem of the Day

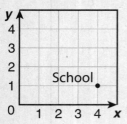

The library is located 2 units up and 3 units left of the school. What are the coordinates of the library?

Number Sense

How can you use the Distributive Property to multiply 15 × 21?

Word of the Day

integer

Which of the following numbers are *integers*?

$4, 2.5, -7, 0, \frac{1}{2}, -3$

_____

_____

_____

Facts Practice

Fill in the missing number.

1. $(4 - 1) \times$ ____ $= 3 \times 7$

2. $3 \times (5 + 3) = 3 \times$ ____

3. $23 \times 651 =$ ____ $\times 651$

4. $2 \times 9 \times 6 =$ ____ $\times 6$

5. $8 \times 4 = 8 \times (24 \div$ ____$)$

6. $(144 \div 12) \times 10 = 12 \times$ ____

Name _____ Date _____

Graphs of Functions

CA Standards
KEY MG 2.0, **KEY** MG 2.1

Solve.

1. Complete the table to 6 boxes. Then write the pairs of data as ordered pairs. Record the number of boxes as the first coordinate. Graph the function.

Boxes of mugs $y = 5x$	
Number of boxes (x)	Number of mugs (y)
1	5
2	10
3	
4	
5	
6	

_____

_____

Use the graph at the right for problems 2–3. Assume the points lie on the same line.

Cats and Legs

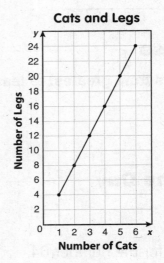

2. How many more legs do 5 cats have than 3 cats?

_____

3. How many cats have a total of 12 legs? How can you tell from the graph?

_____

_____

_____

 **Test Practice**

Circle the the letter of the correct answer

4. A line follows the rule $y = 2x$. Which of the following ordered pairs lies on this line?

   A (4, 6)   **C** (5, 10)

   B (8, 4)   **D** (0, 2)

5. Which ordered pair does not lie on the line determined by the function rule $y = 4x$?

   A (1, 4)   **C** (2, 8)

   B (3, 12)   **D** (4, 15)

Writing Math Let x stand for the number of cats and let y stand for the number of legs in the graph above. Write a rule in the form "$y =$" for finding the number of legs on x cats. Explain.

_____

_____

Graph Equations

Problem of the Day
KEY **MG 2.1**

Make a list of ordered pairs from the function table below and use Workmat 6 to plot the points. Draw a line to connect the points and predict how many tennis balls would come in 5 cans.

Number of cans (c)	Number of tennis balls (t)
0	0
2	6
4	12

Number Sense
KEY **NS 1.2**

Order the numbers from greatest to least.

$3.2, \frac{7}{2}, 2\frac{3}{4}, 3\frac{1}{4}, 2.9$

Number of the Day
NS 4.2

64

Draw a factor tree for the number 64.

_____

_____

_____

Facts Practice
KEY **NS 3.3**

Multiply.

1. 816×22 2. 337×45 3. 525×17

4. 198×36 5. 724×83 6. 644×51

Graph Equations

CA Standards
KEY MG 2.0, KEY MG 2.1

Use the equation to make a function table. Then on a separate piece of graph paper, graph the equation.

1. $y = 2x - 1$

Input (x)	Output (y)

2. $y = 6x - 2$

Input (x)	Output (y)

3. $y = 4x + 4$

Input (x)	Output (y)

4. $y = 5x - 5$

Input (x)	Output (y)

Test Practice

Circle the letter of the correct answer.

5. Dara is trying to graph the function $y = 3x + 3$. Which of the following ordered pairs will not be on her graph?

   A (0, 3)　　　　**C** (1, 6)

   B (2, 9)　　　　**D** (3, 11)

6. Shilpa plotted the points (1, 3), (2, 5) and (3, 7). Which could be the function rule she is trying to graph?

   A $y = x + 2$　　　　**C** $y = x + 3$

   B $y = 2x$　　　　**D** $y = 2x + 1$

Writing Math Thomas plotted the points (0, 4), (1, 5) and (2, 6) to represent a function rule. Find the function rule. If he extends his line, will it contain the ordered pair (7, 10)? Explain why or why not.

_____

_____

_____

Problem Solving: Use a Graph

Problem of the Day ———————————————————— KEY MG 2.1

Does the point (1, 2) lie on the graph of the equation $y = 5x + 2$?

Number Sense ———————————————————————— NS 4.1

Use divisibility rules to tell if 2, 3, 5, 9, and 10 are factors of the given numbers.

1. 85

2. 60

3. 108

Word of the Day ————————————————————————— MR 2.3

equivalent

Is it possible to find all the *equivalent* fractions for $\frac{1}{2}$?

_____

_____

_____

Facts Practice ——————————————————————————— KEY NS 1.3

Round each number to the nearest hundred. Then estimate the difference.

1. 395,209 − 49,294   **2.** 87,452 − 981   **3.** 6,130 − 3,756

4. 439 − 368   **5.** 250,448 − 193,194   **6.** 67,272 − 1,829

Daily Routines

212

Use with Chapter 21, Lesson 5

Name _____ Date _____

Problem Solving: Use a Graph

CA Standards
KEY MG 2.1, MR 2.3

Georgia works at her ceramics studio. Each day, after taking time to set up, she makes plates. The graph shows the relationship between the number of plates completed and the number of hours worked.

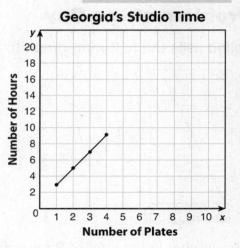

Georgia's Studio Time

1. How many hours will it take Georgia to complete

   3 plates? _____

2. How much more time will it take her to complete
   5 plates than 2 plates?

   _____

3. Georgia spent 6 hours at her studio. She sells all the plates that she completed in that time. If she sells each plate for $20, how much money does she make?

   _____

4. Georgia spent 9 hours working in her studio each day for 5 days. How many plates did she complete?

   _____

5. If you extend the line, will the point (8, 17) be on it? _____

Test Practice

Circle the letter of the correct answer.

The graph at the right shows the number of dogs walked based on the number of hours Tom worked.

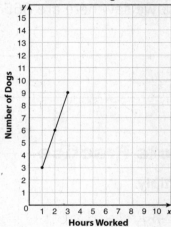

Number of Dogs Walked

6. How many dogs can Tom walk in an hour?

   A 1   **B** 2   **c** 3   **D** 6

7. If Tom gets paid $10 for each dog that he walks, how much money can he make in 3 hours?

   A $10   **B** $30   **c** $60   **D** $90

Writing Math Explain how to use the graph of "Georgia's Studio Time" to find the number of hours required to produce 15 plates.

_____

_____

Name _____ Date _____

Hands On: Graph Ordered Pairs of Integers

Problem of the Day ———————————————— MR 2.3

Felino uses the following graph to find the cost of walnuts per pound.

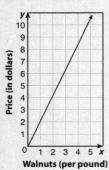

About what is the cost of 3 pounds of walnuts?

Number Sense Review ———————————————— KEY NS 1.1

Write the expanded number in word form. The values are not in order.

300 + 40,000,000 + 500,000 + 2 + 6,000,000 + 70,000

Number of the Day ———————————————— NS 2.2

365.25

The actual number of days in a year is about 365.25. Why do you
think we say there are 365 days in a year?

_____

_____

Facts Practice ———————————————— KEY NS 3.0

Multiply.

1. 730 × 8   **2.** 359 × 4   **3.** 214 × 7

4. 1,977 × 6   **5.** 9,415 × 2   **6.** 8,802 × 5

Name _____ Date _____

Hands On: Graph Ordered Pairs of Integers

CA Standards
KEY MG 2.0, **KEY** NS 1.8

Find the point in the coordinate plane.

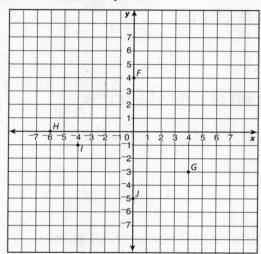

1. (6, 0). Label it *A*.

2. (⁻4, 3). Label it *B*.

3. (5, 5). Label it *C*.

4. (⁻2, ⁻4). Label it *D*.

5. (6, ⁻7). Label it *E*.

Write the coordinates of the point.

6. *F* _____

7. *G* _____

8. *H* _____

9. *I* _____

10. *J* _____

Test Practice

Circle the letter of the correct answer.

11. Which point is on the *x*-axis?

   A (4, 0)   **C** (⁻6, ⁻7)

   B (3, 5)   **D** (0, 4)

12. Which point is on the *y*-axis?

   A (8, 0)   **C** (8, 8)

   B (⁻8, ⁻8)   **D** (0, 8)

Writing Math Where do you locate negative numbers on the coordinate plane?

_____

_____

Graph Ordered Pairs of Integers

Problem of the Day

If a point is exactly 2 units away from the origin on one of the axes of the coordinate plane, what could its coordinates be?

Number Sense

Use Workmat 4 to decide if $\frac{7}{12}$ is to the left or right of $\frac{2}{3}$ on the number line.

Word of the Day — KEY NS 4.2

composite number

During the day when you come across different numbers, think about whether or not they are *composite numbers* and what makes them composite.

_____

_____

_____

Facts Practice

Find the missing number.

1. 4 c = _____ pt

2. _____ T = 6,000 lb

3. _____ gal = 40 pt

4. 6 qt = _____ c

5. 3 lb = _____ oz

6. _____ qt = 10 gal

Name _____ Date _____

Graph Ordered Pairs of Integers

CA Standards
KEY MG 2.0, **KEY** NS 1.8

Find, mark, and label the following points on the coordinate plane.

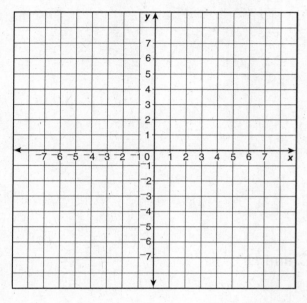

1. A (⁻4, 5)   **2.** B (0, ⁻2)

3. C (⁻3, ⁻7)   **4.** D (6, 3)

5. E (3, ⁻5)   **6.** F (⁻2, ⁻3)

7. G (5, 6)   **8.** H (⁻5, 3)

9. I (0, 6)   **10.** J (⁻7, 0)

Circle the letter of the correct answer.

11. Which point is below the x-axis?

   A (0, 12)   **C** (⁻2, 7)

   B (4, ⁻6)   **D** (8, 5)

12. Which point is on the x-axis?

   A (5, ⁻5)   **C** (⁻11, 0)

   B (6, 7)   **D** (3, ⁻12)

 Writing Math Explain where (⁻2, ⁻8) is on the coordinate plane.

_____

Lengths of Horizontal and Vertical Segments

Problem of the Day ———————————————————— KEY MG 2.0

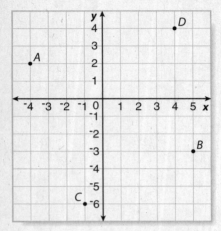

Write the ordered pairs for *A, B, C*, and *D*.

Algebra and Functions ——————————————————— KEY AF 2.0

**Write an expression equal to 13 using all four operations and at
least one set of parentheses.**

Number of the Day ———————————————————— MR 1.1

$\frac{9}{4}$

Write three different facts about the fraction $\frac{9}{4}$.

_____

_____

_____

Facts Practice ——————————————————————— KEY NS 3.0

Use mental math to multiply.

1. 48 × 100   2. 6,000 × 9   3. 80 × 30

4. 100,000 × 70   5. 20 × 12,000   6. 500 × 400

218
 Use with Chapter 22, Lesson 3

Name _____ Date _____

Lengths of Horizontal and Vertical Line Segments

CA Standards
KEY MG 2.2, **KEY** MG 2.3

Graph each pair of points. Find the length of the line segment that connects each pair of points.

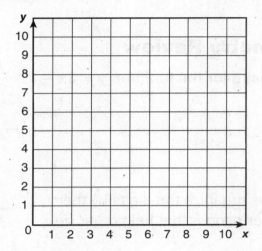

1. (0, 1) (6, 1) _____

2. (10, 1) (10, 9) _____

3. (4, 3) (4, 9) _____

4. (2, 2) (2, 8) _____

5. (1, 10) (9, 10) _____

6. (0, 0) (10, 0) _____

7. (1, 6) (9, 6) _____

8. (0, 2) (0, 10) _____

Test Practice

Circle the letter of the correct answer.

9. What is the distance between (2, 1) and (2, 8)?

   A 0 units   **C** 4 units

   B 7 units   **D** 9 units

10. What is the distance between (3, 0) and (9, 0)?

   A 0 units   **C** 3 Units

   B 6 units   **D** 12 units

Writing Math How can you use subtraction to find the length of a vertical or horizontal line segment in the coordinate grid?

_____

_____

_____

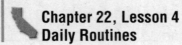
Line Segments in the Coordinate Grid

Problem of the Day ———————————————— KEY MG 2.3

How many units long is the line segment that connects the points whose ordered pairs are (2, 8) and (2, 3)?

Measurement and Geometry Review ———————— KEY MG 2.1

What are three different ordered pairs for the function $y = 3x - 5$?

Word of the Day ———————————————————— MR 1.1

period

A *period* in a place-value chart helps organize the digits by their value. Are you familiar with any other *periods* that help organize information?

_____

_____

_____

Facts Practice ———————————————————— NS 4.1

Find all the factors.

1. 95   **2.** 54   **3.** 19

4. 60   **5.** 88   **6.** 37

Name _____ Date _____

Line Segments in the Coordinate Grid

Graph and connect each pair of points. Then count units to find the length of the line segment.

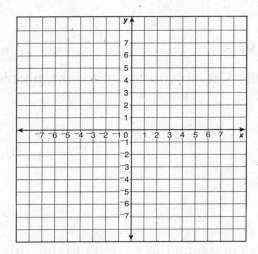

1. (5, 7) (5, ⁻5) _____

2. (⁻7, 0) (4, 0) _____

3. (0, ⁻6) (0, 5) _____

4. (⁻6, 2) (6, 2) _____

Subtract to find the length of the line segment that connects each pair of points.

5. (3, ⁻7) (6, ⁻7) _____

6. (⁻2, 9) (⁻2, 4) _____

7. (⁻8, 7) (⁻8, 1) _____

8. (1, ⁻7) (8, ⁻7) _____

Circle the letter of the correct answer.

9. The line segment connecting which two points is 3 units long?

   A (⁻1, 4) (⁻1, 7)   C (2, 5) (8, 5)

   B (0, 0) (3, 3)   D (0, 3) (3, 6)

10. How long is the line segment connecting (⁻1, ⁻6) and (7, ⁻6)?

    A 2 units   C 6 units

    B 7 units   D 8 units

Writing Math Where on the coordinate grid is a point whose coordinates are (–, +), for example, (⁻2, 7)?

_____

Problem Solving: Field Trip

Problem of the Day

Use Workmat 7 to plot and connect the points (−1, −3) and (7, −3).
What is the length of the line segment?

Number Sense Review

Explain what Jeff did wrong when he solved the following problem.

$$\begin{array}{r} 58 \\ 3\overline{)1,524} \end{array}$$

Number of the Day

15

Think up a division word problem in which the solution to the problem
is 15.

_____

_____

Facts Practice

Round to the nearest tenth and estimate the sums.

1. 34.15 + 46.25

2. 101.94 + 5.81

3. 7.67 + 52.14

4. 82.46 + 12.43

5. 200.01 + 73.59

6. 415.21 + 315.07

Hands On: Collect and Organize Data

Problem of the Day ——————————————————— NS 1.6

Write a decimal equivalent for $\frac{3}{4}$.

Number Sense Review ——————————————— KEY NS 1.9

Use Workmat 4 to plot these fractions:

$\frac{3}{4}$, $1\frac{7}{8}$, $1\frac{1}{2}$, $\frac{1}{4}$

Word of the Day ——————————————————— MR 2.4

Associative Property of Addition

Using the numbers 1, 4, and 6, write an equation showing the
Associative Property of Addition.

_____

_____

_____

Facts Practice ——————————————————— KEY NS 3.2

Solve.

1. $60 \div 5$ **2.** 4×7 **3.** $72 \div 8$

4. $36 \div 6$ **5.** 11×3

Hands On: Collect and Organize Data

CA Standards
SDAP 1.1, SDAP 1.0

Brian conducted a survey of his classmates' favorite sports. The table at the right shows the results of his survey. Each person picked one favorite sport.

Sport	Tally	Number
Soccer	卌 卌 卌 卌 IIII	24
Hockey	卌 III	8
Baseball	卌 卌 I	11
Track	卌 卌 卌 卌	20
Basketball	卌 卌 卌 II	17

Use the tally chart for Problems 1–4.

1. How many classmates answered the question?

   _____

2. What is the most popular sport? What is the least popular sport?

   _____

3. Did more people surveyed like track than basketball? Explain.

   _____

4. Did more than half of the people surveyed choose soccer? Explain.

   _____

 **Test Practice**

Circle the letter of the correct answer.

5. Which set of tally marks correctly represents the number 8?

   A IIII IIII   C 卌 III

   B 卌 IIII   D 卌 II

6. Kerry surveyed her family about their favorite month. Three said July, four said December and two said September. What part of the total number like July best?

   A one-third   C one-fourth

   B one-half   D two-thirds

Writing Math Suppose Leslie wanted to find out which sport is most popular at her school. Would it make sense for her to survey only the members of the football team? Why or why not?

_____

_____

_____

Median and Mode

Problem of the Day ——————————————— SDAP 1.0

What is the difference between the number of students who chose comedy as their favorite type of movie and the number of students who chose animation?

What is your Favorite Type of Movie?	
Answer	Tally
Action	‖‖ ‖‖ ‖
Comedy	‖‖ ‖‖ ‖‖
Animation	‖‖ ‖

Number Sense Review ——————————————— KEY NS 3.2

If you fill 14 water balloons with exactly 500 milliliters of water in each, how many liters of water will you have used?

Word of the Day ——————————————— NS 1.6

decimal

What *decimals* do you see during your day?

_____

_____

_____

Facts Practice ——————————————— KEY NS 1.8

Compare.

1. −3 __ −7

2. −9 __ 1

3. 2 __ −2

4. −15 __ −16

5. −8 __ 0

6. 5 __ −6

Median and Mode

CA Standards
SDAP 1.1, SDAP 1.2

Order the data from least to greatest. Find the mode, median, and any outliers.

1. 14, 20, 14, 2

_____

2. 7, 13, 10, 7, 18, 52

_____

3. 22, 6, 12, 84, 20, 20

_____

4. 55, 42, 61, 5, 61, 53, 62

_____

5. 73, 13, 10, 17, 10, 22, 12

_____

Test Practice

Circle the letter of the correct answer.

6. Which number is the mode of the data below?
13, 14, 9, 17, 14, 8, 18, 10, 6

  A 14   **B** 10   **C** 18   **D** 13

7. Jessica collected 87 glass bottles on Monday, 58 on Tuesday, 92 on Wednesday, 72 on Thursday, and 61 on Friday. What is the median number of bottles she collected?

  A 58   **B** 87   **C** 72   **D** 61

Writing Math Howard was asked to find the mode in problem 7 above. He said there wasn't one. Is he correct? Explain.

_____

_____

Hands On: Double Bar Graphs

Problem of the Day ——————————————————— AF 1.1

Set A	Set B
20	11
18	10
16	9
14	8

What is the number Set B when Set A is 2?

Number Sense Review ——————————————————— NS 2.1

Using a blank workmat, draw a quick picture to find 2.25 − 1.07.

Number of the Day ——————————————————— NS 4.1

30

Write a fact family for the number 30.

_____

_____

_____

Facts Practice ——————————————————— KEY NS 3.0

Solve.

1. 65 + 230

2. 118 − 71

3. 422 + 229 − 584

4. 9,090 − 5,664

5. 26,781 + 413 − 2,085

Name _____ Date _____

Hands On: Double Bar Graphs

CA Standards
SDAP 1.3, SDAP 1.0

Arnold made a chart to show his sales for the two most popular items at his painting studio. The table at the right shows the sales for each item.

Number of Items Sold			
Item	2002	2003	2004
Portraits	60	70	70
Landscapes	60	65	75

**Use the table on the right to make a double bar graph.
Use the graph for Problems 1–4.**

1. What interval did you choose for your graph? Explain your choice.

   _____

2. In which year were there more landscapes sold than portraits?

   _____

3. Which item did Arnold sell the same number of in 2003 and 2004?

   _____

4. Which item showed a steady increase in sales for each year?

   _____

 **Test Practice**

Circle the letter of the correct answer.

5. Which could you show with a double bar graph?

   A The height of the world's 7 tallest mountains

   B The birthdays of all the students in one class

   C The number of centimeters a corn plant and a tomato plant grew each week

   D The number of inches of rainfall your hometown received each month

6. Which could you NOT show with a double bar graph?

   A The number of students in your class and another class

   B The distance from the sun of each of the 8 planets

   C The height of you and your brother

   D The number of days it snowed in January and February

Writing Math Matilda wanted to change the correct choice from problem 6 above so it could be shown as a double bar graph. Is this possible? Give an example.

_____

_____

Name _____ Date _____

Read and Understand Line Graphs

Problem of the Day ———————————————— SDAP 1.3

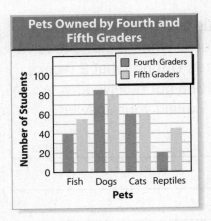

Which animal do more fourth graders own than fifth graders?

Measurement and Geometry Review ———————— KEY MG 2.0

Use Workmat 7 to plot the points *A* (4, 7), *B* (−2, 3), *C* (−5, −1), and
D (1, −6).

Number of the Day ———————————————— NS 4.1

60

The ancient Babylonians used a number system based on the number
60 because of its many factors. What are the factors of 60?

_____

_____

_____

Facts Practice ———————————————————— NS 2.1

Add or subtract.

1. 30.1 − 5.6   **2.** 15.6 + 28.3   **3.** 167.5 − 140.2

4. 77.4 + 11.8   **5.** 62.7 − 5.9   **6.** 229.2 + 330.8

Name _____ Date _____

Read and Understand Line Graphs

CA Standards
SDAP 1.0, SDAP 1.3

The graph below shows the height of a ficus tree. Use the
graph to answer Problems 1–4.

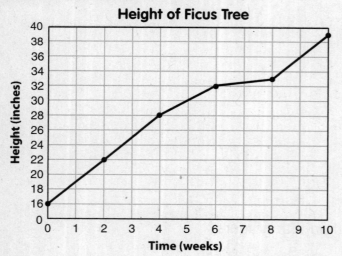

Height of Ficus Tree

1. The ficus tree grew more slowly
   for 2 weeks when it didn't receive
   any water. During what 2 weeks
   did the tree not receive any
   water? Explain your answer.

   _____

   _____

   _____

   _____

2. What was the greatest amount of growth for any 2-week period? _____

3. How tall was the tree at week 4? _____

4. When was the tree 22 inches tall? _____

Test Practice

Circle the letter of the correct answer.

5. At what week on the graph above was
   the ficus tree 32 inches tall?

   A week 5   c week 7

   B week 6   D week 8

6. What would you expect the ficus tree's
   height to be at week 11?

   A 38 inches   c 42 inches

   B 40 inches   D 46 inches

Writing Math Sam made a line graph of the growth of an ivy
plant on the wall behind his house. The growth over 4 weeks was 5
inches, 10 inches, 15 inches and 20 inches. He made the intervals in
inches in multiples of 3s. Was this a good decision? Why or why not?

_____

_____

Problem Solving: Show Data in Different Ways

Problem of the Day ————————————————— SDAP 1.3

How many fewer bikes were sold in year 3 than in year 2?

Measurement and Geometry Review ————————— MG 1.0

What would the perimeter of a rectangle be with a width of 7 feet and a length of 8 feet?

Word of the Day ————————————————————— KEY **NS 3.2**

divisible

Throughout the day, when you come across a number, think of at least one number, other than 1, that it is *divisible* by.

_____

_____

_____

Facts Practice ———————————————— KEY **MG 2.2**, KEY **MG 2.3**

Find the length of each line segment.

1. (12, 5), (4, 5)

2. (−3, 4), (−3, 10)

3. (1, 1), (1, 4)

4. (6, −9), (15, −9)

5. (0, 5), (0, 0)

6. (11, 2), (10, 2)

Name _____ Date _____

Problem Solving:
Show Data in Different Ways

CA Standards
MR 2.3, SDAP 1.0

Use the double bar graph to answer questions 1–3. The graph compares the number of cars sold by Tom and Bill, two competing car dealers.

1. In which year did Tom sell more cars than Bill?

   _____

2. How many more cars than Tom did Bill

   sell in 2004? _____

3. What was the total number of cars Bill sold in 2004, 2005 and 2006?

   _____

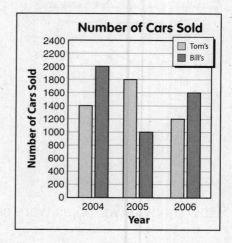

Test Practice

Circle the letter of the correct answer.

Use the double bar graph to answer questions 4 and 5.

4. How many goals did the girls' team score in Game 3?

   A 3   C 4

   B 5   D 8

5. How many more goals did the boys' team score in Game 1?

   A 1   C 2

   B 3   D 4

Writing Math Describe a set of data for which a scatter plot would not be an appropriate representation.

_____

_____

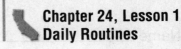
Hands On: Probability and Outcomes

Problem of the Day ———————————— SDAP 1.0

Alana wants to make a graph to show the daily high temperatures for the last week. What type of graph would best show this information?

Statistics, Data Analysis and Probability Review —— SDAP 1.2

Write a set with 5 data points which have a median of 8 and a mode of 2.

Word of the Day ———————————— NS 1.5

fraction

In what situations do you use fractions in your everyday life?

_____

_____

_____

Facts Practice ———————————— NS 1.0

Write the value of the underlined digit.

1. 2.8<u>7</u>

2. 12.0<u>9</u>

3. 124.<u>4</u>

4. <u>4</u>1,389

5. 373.<u>3</u>5

6. 6,<u>4</u>09,395

Hands On: Probability and Outcomes

CA Standards
SDAP 2.0, SDAP 2.2

Write *certain, likely, unlikely,* or *impossible* to describe the
probability that a spin will land on a shaded area.

1.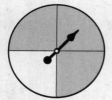

_____

2.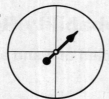

_____

3.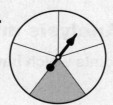

_____

Test Practice

Circle the letter of the correct answer.

4. From this tally chart, which two colored
   marbles are you *unlikely* to pick?

   A red and green   **C** pink and purple

   B blue and red   **D** blue and green

Picking Marbles		
Outcome	**Tally**	**Number**
Red	卌 卌 ‖	12
Blue	卌	5
Green	卌 ‖	7

5. If 8 black marbles and 13 white
   marbles are placed into a bag, what
   is the probability of picking a white
   marble from the bag?

   A likely   **C** certain

   B unlikely   **D** impossible

Writing Math Fiona did problem 4 above and chose *C*, pink
and purple, as unlikely marbles. Is her answer right or wrong? Explain.

_____

_____

_____

Name _____ Date _____

Represent Outcomes

Problem of the Day ——————————————— NS 1.5

Write 3 equivalent fractions to $\frac{1}{3}$.

Number Sense Review ——————————————— KEY

Use Workmat 2 to write four hundred nine million, sixteen.

Number of the Day ——————————————— NS 1.6

$6\frac{1}{2}$

Model $6\frac{1}{2}$ with a picture and then write the number as a decimal.

_____

_____

_____

Facts Practice ——————————————— NS 1.5

Add or subtract.

1. $\frac{1}{4} + \frac{2}{4}$ **2.** $7\frac{2}{3} - 1\frac{1}{3}$

3. $1\frac{4}{9} + \frac{6}{27}$ **4.** $8\frac{1}{5} - 3\frac{4}{5}$

Name _____ Date _____

Represent Outcomes

CA Standards
SDAP 2.1, SDAP 2.2

The tree diagram shows the possible outcomes when a coin is tossed and a three-part spinner is spun. Use the tree diagram for Problems 1–2.

1. Make a grid to show the same outcomes.

Coin	Spinner	Outcome
heads	white	heads, white
	black	heads, black
	striped	heads, striped
tails	white	tails, white
	black	tails, black
	striped	tails, striped

2. Write the probability of tails and striped as a fraction and in words.

_____

Use the spinners for Problem 3.

3. Draw a grid to show all the possible outcomes of spins on both spinners.

Test Practice

Circle the letter of the correct answer.

4. Two number cubes with the faces labeled 1–6 on each cube are rolled. Out of the possible outcomes of the rolls of both cubes, what is the probability that the sum is 6?

   A $\frac{1}{2}$ C $\frac{1}{6}$

   B $\frac{5}{12}$ D $\frac{5}{36}$

5. Mary can wear a red shirt or a green shirt, blue jeans or black jeans, and white shoes or orange shoes. How many different ways she can dress?

   A 4   C 8

   B 6   D 12

Writing Math Dan did problem 4 above and felt the answer should have been $\frac{6}{36}$. Do you agree? Why or why not?

_____

_____

_____

Problem Solving: Field Trip

Problem of the Day

Write 9.73 in word form.

Measurement Review

Write how many pounds.

1. 160 ounces

2. 3,200 ounces

3. 4 tons

Word of the Day

composite

Give six examples of composite numbers.

_____

_____

_____

Facts Practice

Multiply or divide.

1. 53 ÷ 6   2. 16 × 9   3. 71 × 3

4. 81 ÷ 3   5. 61 ÷ 8   6. 86 × 7

Name _____ Date _____

Hands On: Points, Lines, and Line Segments

Problem of the Day ————————————————— SDAP 1.3

The line graph below shows the high temperature over 5 days.

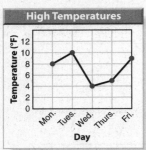

What is the difference between the temperatures on Tuesday and the temperature on Wednesday? Express the difference as a positive or negative integer.

Number Sense Review ————————————————— NS 2.1

Write a subtraction problem with decimals through the hundredths, and a difference of 4.87.

Number of the Day ————————————————— NS 4.1

60

List all the factors for 60.

_____

_____

_____

Facts Practice ————————————————— KEY

Find each product.

1. 24 × 46   **2.** 17 × 89   **3.** 54 × 92

4. 33 × 402   **5.** 61 × 534   **6.** 72 × 806

Hands On: Points, Lines, and Line Segments

Use words and symbols to name each figure.

1. A •
_____

2.
_____

3.
_____

4. X •
_____

Write *parallel*, *intersecting*, or *perpendicular* to best describe the relationship between each pair of lines.

5.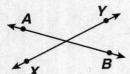

6.

7.

_____   _____   _____

Test Practice

Circle the letter of the correct answer.

8. Which best describes the lines $\overleftrightarrow{AB}$ and $\overleftrightarrow{CD}$?

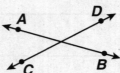

A parallel   **C** intersecting

B point   **D** perpendicular

9. Which best describes the geometric figure below?

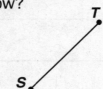

A line *ST*   **C** line segment

B perpendicular   **D** right angle *ST*
line

 Writing Math Can two lines intersect and be perpendicular? Draw a picture to explain.

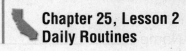
Name _____ Date _____

Rays and Angles

Problem of the Day ———————————————————— MG 3.1

Which two lines or segments appear perpendicular in this drawing?

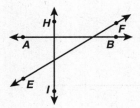

Number Sense Review ———————————————————— KEY NS 1.1

How do you write this number in word form?

21,444,560

Show in standard form.

Nine million, eight hundred thousand, four hundred fifty-nine.

Word of the Day ———————————————————— NS 4.0

even number

Give two examples of a 5-digit number that is even.

_____

_____

_____

Facts Practice ———————————————————— KEY NS 3.1

Solve.

1. 359 − 176   **2.** 832 − 498   **3.** 703 + 617

4. 934 − 589   **5.** 510 − 367   **6.** 914 + 98

Rays and Angles

CA Standards
MG 3.5, MG 3.0

Name each angle in three ways. Then classify the angle as *acute*, *obtuse*, *right*, or *straight*.

1.

_____

2.

_____

3.

_____

4.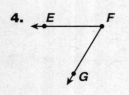

_____

5.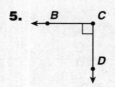

_____

6.

_____

Test Practice

Circle the the letter of the correct answer.

7. What kind of angle is shown?

A acute   C straight

B obtuse   D right

8. What kind of angle is shown?

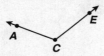

A acute   C raight

B obtuse   D right

Writing Math Explain how the face and hands of a round clock can show different types of angles.

_____

_____

_____

_____

_____

_____

_____

Polygons and Quadrilaterals

Problem of the Day ————————————————— MG 3.5

Is this angle acute or obtuse?

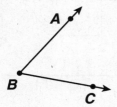

Number Sense Review ———————————————— KEY NS 3.2

Fill in the missing numbers.

7 kg = _____ g

10 kg = _____ g

2000 g = _____ kg

9000 g = _____ kg

Number of the Day ————————————————— MG 3.5

90

Draw a picture of an angle that is a right angle, or 90 degrees.

_____

_____

_____

Facts Practice ————————————————————— KEY NS 3.2

Multiply.

1. 12 × 12   **2.** 9 × 8   **3.** 11 × 5

4. 10 × 11   **5.** 9 × 12   **6.** 12 × 5

Name _____ Date _____

Polygons and Quadrilaterals

CA Standards
MG 3.8, MG 3.0

**Name each polygon. If the polygon is a quadrilateral,
write all names that apply.**

1.

_____

_____

_____

2.

_____

_____

_____

3.

_____

_____

_____

4.

_____

_____

_____

5.

_____

_____

_____

6.

_____

_____

_____

7.

_____

_____

_____

8.

_____

_____

_____

Test Practice

Circle the letter of the correct answer.

9. What kind of shape is shown?

A quadrilateral   **C** hexagon

B triangle   **D** octagon

10. What kind of shape is shown?

A rectangle   **C** pentagon

B rhombus   **D** trapezoid

Writing Math Describe the similarities and differences
between a rhombus and a parallelogram.

_____

_____

_____

Classify Triangles

Problem of the Day ————————————————————— MG 3.8

What is the name of this shape?

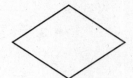

Number Sense Review ——————————————————— KEY NS 1.2

Put these numbers in order from greatest to least:

980,001

6,789,122

78,998

156,894,543

98,001

158,097

Number of the Day ——————————————————— KEY NS 3.0

180

Write three addition sentences with three addends that have a sum of 180.

_____

_____

_____

Facts Practice ——————————————————————— KEY NS 3.2

Give a related problem from the same fact family.

1. 18 ÷ 2 = 9   **2.** 8 × 8 = 64

3. 10 × 5 = 50   **4.** 24 ÷ 6 = 4

Name _____ Date _____

Classify Triangles

CA Standards
MG 3.7, MG 3.0

Tell whether each triangle appears to be *equilateral, isosceles,* or *scalene.*

1.

2.

3.

4.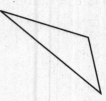

_____ _____ _____ _____

5.

6.

7.

8.

_____ _____ _____ _____

Test Practice

Circle the letter of the correct answer.

9. What kind of triangle is shown?

A right isosceles   **C** acute isosceles

B obtuse scalene   **D** equilateral

10. What kind of triangle is shown?

A right isosceles   **C** obtuse scalene

B acute isosceles   **D** equilateral

Writing Math Describe as clearly and briefly as possible the differences among equilateral, isosceles, and scalene triangles.

_____

_____

_____

_____

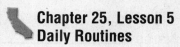
Circles

Problem of the Day ———————————————————— MG 3.7

Mei Lin has a triangular flower bed. The sides measure 6 feet, 5 feet and 5 feet. What type of triangle is Mei Lin's garden?

Statistics, Data Analysis and Probability Review ——— SDAP 1.1

Write a question for a survey whose results would be best displayed on a bar graph.

Word of the Day ———————————————————————— MG 3.0

tri-

What words can you think of which start with tri? What do these words have in common?

_____

_____

_____

Facts Practice ———————————————————————————— AF 1.1

Solve each expression for $n = 12$.

1. $5n - 35$ **2.** $\frac{n}{2} + 8$ **3.** $50 - n + 30$

4. $3n \div 2$ **5.** $n - 5 + 29$ **6.** $(8 + n) \times 2$

Circles

CA Standards
MG 3.2, MG 3.5

Name the part of each circle that is given. Write *center, radius,* or *diameter.*

1. point *A*

_____

2. segment *AB*

_____

3. segment *AB*

_____

4. point *X*

_____

5. segment *XY*

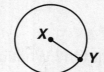

_____

6. segment *XY*

_____

 Test Practice

Circle the letter of the correct answer.

7. How many degrees is a quarter turn on a circle?

A 180°   **C** 360°

B 90°   **D** 270°

8. How many degrees is a three-quarter turn of a circle?

A 360°   **C** 90°

B 180°   **D** 270°

Writing Math If a circle has a radius that is 8 cm long, how long is the circle's diameter? Explain how you know this.

_____

Problem Solving: Field Trip

Problem of the Day ——————————————— MG 3.2

A circle has a radius *DE* that is 3 inches long. How long is radius *DB* and diameter *AC* on the same circle?

Measurement and Geometry Review ———————— MG 3.7

Draw an isosceles triangle at the top of your whiteboard. Below this draw a scalene triangle. Below this draw an acute triangle.

Word of the Day ——————————————— MR 3.3

square

What makes a polygon a square? What makes a number a square number?

_____

_____

_____

Facts Practice ——————————————— KEY NS 3.2

Find each quotient.

1. 98 ÷ 4   2. 128 ÷ 8   3. 492 ÷ 3

4. 548 ÷ 5   5. 387 ÷ 6   6. 609 ÷ 7

Hands On: Line Symmetry

Problem of the Day ——————————————————— MG 3.7

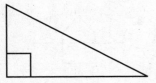

Classify the triangle shown above.

Number Sense ——————————————————— KEY NS 1.9

Use Workmat 4 to plot the following integers and fractions.

$-3, -\frac{1}{2}, 4, \frac{2}{9}$

Word of the Day ——————————————————— SDAP 1.0

line graph

Throughout the day, see how many examples of line graphs you can find in newspapers and magazines.

_____

_____

_____

Facts Practice ——————————————————— KEY NS 3.4

Multiply.

1. 33×9 **2.** 41×8 **3.** 28×7

4. 53×8 **5.** 188×5 **6.** 91×1

Name _____ Date _____

Hands On: Line Symmetry

Is the dashed line a line of symmetry? Write yes or no.

1.

2.

3.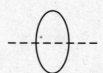

4.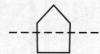

_____   _____   _____   _____

How many lines of symmetry does the figure have?

5.

6.

7.

8.

_____   _____   _____   _____

Test Practice

Circle the letter of the correct answer.

9. How many lines of symmetry does the figure have?

   A 1   **C** 2

   B 3   **D** 6

10. Which letter has a line of symmetry?

    A S   **C** F

    B L   **D** M

Writing Math Tell how you know that η does not have a line of symmetry.

_____

_____

Line or Bilateral Symmetry

Problem of the Day ———————————— MG 3.4

Lupe drew the figure below.

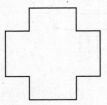

How many lines of symmetry does it have?

Statistics, Data Analysis and Probability ———— SDAP 2.2

On Workmat 6, draw a spinner for which the probability of spinning red would be $\frac{2}{6}$.

Word of the Day ———————————————— NS 4.0

odd

List all the odd numbers between 60 and 80 that are also prime.

_____

_____

_____

Facts Practice ———————————————— NS 2.1

Estimate each sum or difference by rounding the nearest whole number.

1. 80.64 − 8.91   **2.** 12.03 + 7.83   **3.** 54.3 + 8.15

4. 23.07 − 9.8   **5.** 3.64 + 19.06   **6.** 75.19 − 28.44

Line or Bilateral Symmetry

CA Standards
MG 3.0, MG 3.4

Is the dashed line a line of symmetry? Write *yes* or *no*.

1.

_____

2.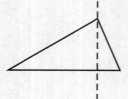

_____

3.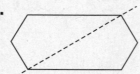

_____

4.

_____

How many lines of symmetry does each figure have?

5.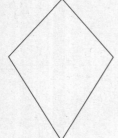

_____

6.

_____

7.

_____

8.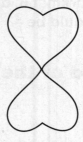

_____

Test Practice

Circle the letter of the correct answer.

9. How many lines of symmetry does the figure have?

A 0   C 1

B 2   D 4

10. Which number has a line of symmetry?

A 3   C 6

B 7   D 9

Writing Math Do all right triangles have a line of symmetry? (You can draw pictures to help you answer the question.)

_____

_____

Rotational Symmetry

Problem of the Day ———————————————————— MG 3.4

Patsy wrote her name in all capital letters below.

PATSY

Which letters have bilateral symmetry?

Measurement and Geometry ———————————————— MG 3.8

Draw a rhombus at the top of your whiteboard. Below the rhombus, draw a trapezoid. Below the trapezoid draw a parallelogram that is not a rectangle.

Number of the Day ———————————————————— MG 3.5

90

How is this number important in geometry?

_____

_____

_____

Facts Practice ————————————————————— KEY AF 1.2

Simplify each expression.

1. $2 \times (14 - 9) + 3$ **2.** $(18 - 6) \div (5 - 2)$ **3.** $50 - 34 \div 2$

4. $84 \div 6 \times 5$ **5.** $10 \times (9 - 3) \div 5$ **6.** $48 - 16 \div 4 \times 7$

Rotational Symmetry

CA Standards
MG 3.4, MG 3.5

Does the figure have rotational symmetry? Write *yes* or *no*.

1.

2.

3.

4.

_____   _____

5.

6.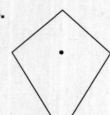

7.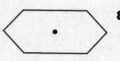

8.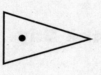

9.

_____   _____   _____   _____   _____

Test Practice

Circle the letter of the correct answer.

10. Which letter has rotational symmetry?

    A I   **C** L

    B E   **D** C

11. Which letter does *not* have rotational symmetry?

    A S   **C** N

    B Z   **D** M

Writing Math This figure does not have rotational symmetry: →. How could you change the figure so that it does have rotational symmetry?

_____

_____

Congruent Figures

Problem of the Day ———————————————— AF 1.1

Solve the equation.

$40 \div x = 8$

Number Sense ———————————————————— KEY NS 3.0

Estimate the product.

1. 89×76

2. 104×98

3. 26×4

Word of the Day ———————————————————— KEY NS 3.2

quotient

Identify the quotient in the following problem.

$$\begin{array}{r} 14 \\ 6\overline{)84} \end{array}$$

_____

_____

_____

Facts Practice ———————————————————— KEY NS 3.4

Estimate using compatible numbers.

1. 27×3

2. 103×4

3. 13×9

4. $89 \div 2$

5. $198 \div 4$

6. $980 \div 11$

Name _____ Date _____

Congruent Figures

CA Standards
MG 3.0, MG 3.3

Do the figures in each pair appear to be congruent? Write *yes* or *no*.

1.

_____

2.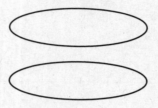

_____

3.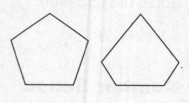

_____

Do figures in the diagrams below appear to be congruent?

4.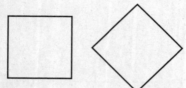

_____

5.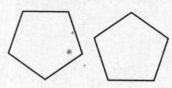

_____

6.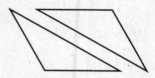

_____

Test Practice

Circle the letter of the correct answer.

7. Which figure appears to be congruent to this figure?

A   C

B   D

8. Which pair of figures appear to be congruent?

A   C

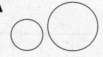

B   D

Writing Math Find two shapes in the room you are in that are congruent. Explain how you know they are congruent.

_____

_____

Problem Solving: Patterns in the Coordinate Grid

Problem of the Day —————————————————— MG 3.3

Which of the triangles shown below are congruent?

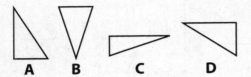

Number Sense ————————————————————————— NS 1.0

Write a number in which the tenths digit and the thousands digit
are a 4, the greatest place value is ten thousands and the digit in
the hundredths is the least digit.

Number of the Day ————————————————————— KEY NS 1.8

⁻8

Describe 3 things which this integer could represent.

_____

_____

_____

Facts Practice ——————————————————————————— NS 4.0

List all the factors of each number.

1. 24   **2.** 38   **3.** 43

4. 54   **5.** 63   **6.** 72

Problem Solving:
Patterns in the Coordinate Grid

CA Standards
MR 1.1, MG 3.0

For questions 1–3 use the pattern below.

1. If the pattern continues, what are the coordinates of the vertices of the fourth triangle?

   _____

2. If the pattern continues, what are the coordinates of the top-left vertex of the sixth triangle?

   _____

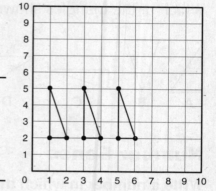

3. Describe the pattern in your own words.

   _____

   _____

 Test Practice

Circle the letter of the correct answer.
Use the pattern to answer questions 4 and 5.

4. If the pattern continues, what are the coordinates of the bottom-left vertex of the fourth triangle?

   A (6, 1)   **C** (7, 1)

   B (6, 4)   **D** (8, 1)

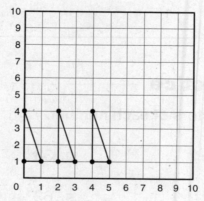

5. Which is the best description of the pattern?

   A The x-coordinates are increased by 2.   **C** The y-coordinates are increased by 2.

   B The x-coordinates are decreased by 2.   **D** The y-coordinates are decreased by 2.

Hands On: Model Perimeter and Area

Problem of the Day ———————————————— NS 2.1, NS 1.6

George lives 2.3 miles from school. Robert lives 4.1 miles from school.
How much farther away does Robert live than George?
Express this answer in fractions

Number Sense Review ———————————————— KEY NS 4.2

On your workmat, write 3 prime numbers and 3 composite numbers.

Number of the Day ———————————————— KEY NS 1.1

5

What is the value of the 5 in each of these numbers?

500,826

4,800,459

5,896,412

Facts Practice ———————————————— KEY NS 3.1

Add or subtract.

1. $569 - 343$ 2. $798 + 754$ 3. $35 + 127$

4. $325 + 252$ 5. $662 - 630$ 6. $902 + 39$

Name _____ Date _____

Hands On: Model Perimeter and Area

CA Standards
MG 1.2, MG 1.3

Find the perimeter and area of each figure. Record your answers in the table.

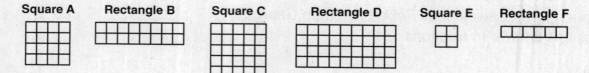

Square A   Rectangle B   Square C   Rectangle D   Square E   Rectangle F

hape	Perimeter	Area
Square A	1. _____ units	2. _____ square units
Rectangle B	3. _____ units	4. _____ square units
Square C	5. _____ units	6. _____ square units
Rectangle D	7. _____ units	8. _____ square units
Square E	9. _____ units	10. _____ square units
Rectangle F	11. _____ units	12. _____ square units

Test Practice

Circle the letter of the correct answers.

13. A square has an area of 64 square units and a perimeter of 32 units. What is the length of one of the sides of the square?

  A 64 units   **C** 8 units

  B 32 units   **D** 24 units

14. Square X has a perimeter of 40 units. Square Y has a perimeter that is half of the perimeter of square X. What is the area of square Y?

  A 20 units   **C** 60 units

  B 25 units   **D** 100 units

Writing Math Janie needs to know the area of a rectangle that is 3 units on one side and 4 units on the top. Tell her how to find the area. Solve the problem.

Use Formulas for Perimeter

Problem of the Day ——————————————————— MG 1.0

Tucker draws a rectangle with a length of 4 units and a width of
2 units. Are the perimeter and area of the rectangle the same?

Statistics, Data and Probability Review ————————— SDAP 2.0

Use the spinner to decide if each outcome
is *certain, likely, unlikely* or *impossible.*

1. landing on red

2. landing on black

3. landing on a color with the letter *e* in
its name

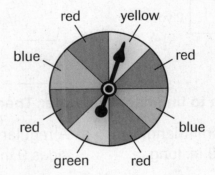

Word of the Day ——————————————————————— MG 3.4

symmetry

Look for different objects during the school day that show *symmetry*.

_____

_____

_____

Facts Practice ———————————————————————— NS 1.0

Add.

1. $\frac{1}{5} + \frac{3}{5}$

2. $\frac{8}{25} + \frac{9}{25}$

3. $\frac{6}{13} + \frac{5}{13}$

4. $\frac{3}{8} + \frac{2}{8}$

5. $\frac{7}{12} + \frac{5}{12}$

6. $\frac{11}{50} + \frac{36}{50}$

Use Formulas for Perimeter

CA Standards
MG 1.4, AF 1.4

Find the perimeter of each polygon.

1. 4 cm

_____

2. 8 in.

4 in.

_____

3. 9 ft

_____

4. 6 yd

2 yd

_____

5. 8 m

_____

6. 3 cm

_____

Write a formula to find each perimeter. Then solve.

7. An equilateral triangle with sides 9 in. long

_____

8. A regular hexagon with sides 9 in. long

_____

9. A regular pentagon with sides 9 in. long

_____

 **Test Practice**

Circle the letter of the correct answers.

10. The perimeter of a regular octagon is 32 in. What is the length of one side of the octagon?

   A 32 in.   C 8 in.

   B 24 in.   D 4 in.

11. A rectangular lawn is 45 feet long and 30 yards wide. What is the perimeter of the lawn in yards?

   A 150 yards   C 96 yards

   B 270 yards   D 90 yards

Writing Math May needs to find the perimeter of a regular octagon with sides 4 inches long. Tell her how to write a formula to find the perimeter. Be sure to explain the numbers you use in the formula. Solve the problem.

_____

_____

_____

Use Formulas for Area

Problem of the Day ——————————————— MG 1.4

Draw a rectangle that has an area of 9 square units and a perimeter of 12 units.

Measurement and Geometry Review ——————— MG 3.0

Use Workmat 1 to draw and label each line segment.

1. 4 centimeters

2. 37 inches

3. 7.5 centimeters

Word of the Day ——————————————————— NS 1.0

decimal

List some places you might see a decimal in everyday life.

_____

_____

Facts Practice ——————————————————— NS 1.2

Order the following from greatest to least.

1. $\frac{1}{4}$, $\frac{17}{4}$, $\frac{3}{4}$, $5\frac{1}{4}$

2. 0.18, 2.13, 0.8, 1.6

3. $\frac{3}{8}$, 1.7, $\frac{4}{5}$, $\frac{20}{10}$

4. $6\frac{1}{4}$, 6.4, $6\frac{3}{5}$, 6.19

Name _____ Date _____

Use Formulas for Area

CA Standards
MG 1.4, AF 1.4

Find the area of each figure.

1.
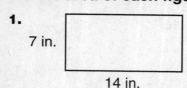
7 in.

14 in.

_____

2.
12 ft

6 ft

_____

3.
11 cm

7 cm

_____

Find the perimeter and area for each rectangle.

4. 4 yd long, 12 yd wide

_____

5. 8 ft long, 6 ft wide

_____

6. 15 cm long, 5 cm wide

_____

7. 13 mi long, 11 mi wide

_____

8. 2 in. long, 36 in. wide

_____

9. 3 m long, 16 m wide

_____

Test Practice

Circle the letter of the correct answers.

10. Which of the figures below has an area that is the same as its perimeter?

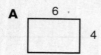
A   6
4

C   4
4

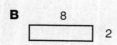
B   8
2

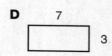
D   7
3

11. Helen wants to carpet her bedroom. Her bedroom is 14 feet long and 12 feet wide. How many square feet of carpeting will Helen need to carpet the entire bedroom?

A 52 square feet

C 60 square feet

B 168 square feet

D 196 square feet

Writing Math Connor added 8 ft² + 8 ft² + 8 ft² + 8 ft² + 8 ft² + 8 ft² to find the perimeter of a large sandbox. Show him another way to find the perimeter of the sandbox. Solve the problem.

_____

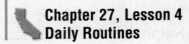
Perimeter and Area of Complex Figures

Problem of the Day ————————————————————— MG 1.4

Jennifer wants to repaint the top of her bedroom desk. The desktop has a length of 3 feet and a width of 2 feet. How much area will Jennifer have to paint?

Number Sense Review ——————————————————— KEY NS 1.8

Benjamin owes David $3. If he gets $5 in his allowance, how much will he have after paying David back?

Number of the Day ————————————————————— SDAP 2.2

6

A number cube has 6 sides. What are the possible outcomes in any rolling experiment when using one number cube labeled 1–6?

_____

_____

_____

Facts Practice ————————————————————————— MG 3.5

Classify each angle as *acute, obtuse,* or *right*.

1. 35°

2. 108°

3. 89°

4. 175°

5. 90°

6. 96°

Name _____ Date _____

Perimeter and Area of Complex Figures

CA Standard
MG 1.4, AF 1.4

Find the perimeter and area of each figure.

1.

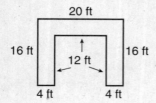

P = _____

A = _____

2.

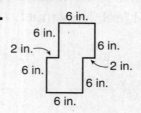

P = _____

A = _____

3.

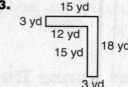

P = _____

A = _____

Find the length of each missing side.

4.

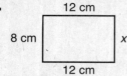

Perimeter = 40 cm

_____

5.

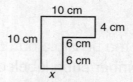

Perimeter = 40 cm

_____

6.

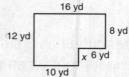

Perimeter = 56 yd

_____

Test Practice

Circle the letter of the correct answers.

7. Alex plans to make a mosaic for his art class. How many one-inch square tiles will he need to cover a surface that is 2 feet × 3 feet?

A 864 tiles   **c** 120 tiles

B 6 tiles   **D** 19 tiles

8. How many one-foot square tiles will it take to cover the surface of the figure in Problem 3?

A 90 tiles   **c** 270 tiles

B 450 tiles   **D** 198 tiles

Writing Math Dimi wants to find the area of the figure in Problem 5. She thinks there are 2 figures that measure 10 cm × 4 cm. She thinks the area of the figure is 40 cm². What has she done wrong? Find the area.

_____

_____

Problem Solving: Use Formulas

Problem of the Day ——————————————— MG 1.4

What is the area of the figure?

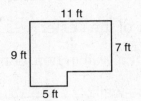

Statistics, Data, and Probability Review ——————— SDAP 1.2

Identify the mode or modes of the
data in the line plot.

Number of Pets Owned						
	X	X				
	X	X				
X	X	X				
X	X	X	X			
X	X	X	X		X
0	1	2	3	4	5	6

Words of the Day ——————————————— MG 3.1

parallel, perpendicular

Which letters of the alphabet are made with both *parallel* and
perpendicular lines?

_____

_____

_____

Facts Practice ——————————————— NS 1.5

Find the fractional part of the number.

1. $\frac{2}{5}$ of 20

2. $\frac{5}{8}$ of 32

3. $\frac{3}{4}$ of 12

4. $\frac{7}{12}$ of 60

5. $\frac{1}{3}$ of 66

6. $\frac{4}{9}$ of 54

Problem Solving: Use Formulas

Use a formula to solve.

1. Suppose that a movie poster is 3 feet wide and 5 feet high.

   What is the perimeter of the poster? _____

2. Melissa wants to paint a wall in her room. The wall measures 10 feet by 15 feet.

   What is the area of the wall? _____

3. A book cover measures 8 inches by 5 inches. What is the maximum amount of space

   for the cover art? _____

4. A fish tank is 16 inches wide. If the height of the tank is 12 inches and the length of

   the tank is 20 inches, what is the perimeter around the bottom of the tank?

   _____

5. A cube-shaped whirlpool measures 4 feet on each side. What is the area of one of

   the sides of the whirlpool? _____

6. Kevin is buying tiles for the bathroom floor. The bathroom is 6 feet by 10 feet. If each
   tile is 1 foot by 1 foot and costs $3, how much money will Kevin spend on tiles for the

   bathroom? _____

Test Practice

Circle the letter of the correct answer.

7. Which represents the area of a room that measures 10 feet by 12 feet?

   A 22 square feet   c 100 square feet

   B 110 square feet   D 120 square feet

8. Which represents the perimeter of a rectangle that is 2 feet by 4 feet?

   A 16 feet   c 8 feet

   B 10 feet   D 12 feet

Writing Math Explain how to use the perimeter formula for a
rectangle to calculate the perimeter of a square.

_____

Hands On: Use Nets to Build Solid Figures

Problem of the Day ———————————————— KEY **NS 3.0**

Gabe found 26 paperback books to buy at the used book sale. Each
book costs 50 cents. How much will all the books cost?

Number Sense ———————————————————— NS 2.1

Anna has sold 46 boxes of cookies for $0.75 each.
How much money has she made?

Word of the Day ———————————————————— MG 3.0

line segment

What is the definition of a line segment?

_____

_____

_____

Facts Practice ———————————————————— NS 1.0

Multiply.

1. $12,000 \times 100$ **2.** $10 \times 120,000$ **3.** 60×10

4. 60×100 **5.** $7,908 \times 10$ **6.** 0×100

Name _____ Date _____

Use Nets to Build Solid Figures

CA Standards
MG 3.6, MR 2.3

Name the solid figure that can be made with the net. Then complete the table.

1.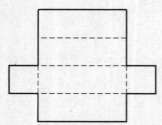

2.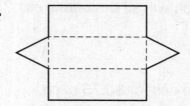

3.

	Solid Figure's Name	Number of Faces	Number of Edges	Number of Vertices
1.				
2.				
3.				

 Test Practice

Circle the letter of the correct answer.

4. Which of the following best represents the shape of a soup can?

   A triangular pyramid   **C** rectangular prism

   B cone   **D** cylinder

5. Which of the following best represents the shape of a cereal box?

   A triangular pyramid   **C** rectangular prism

   B cone   **D** cylinder

Writing Math Describe the faces of a square pyramid.

_____

_____

Solid Figures and Nets

Problem of the Day —————————————————

Write 47,166 in expanded notation.

Number Sense —————————————————————

Compare. Write <, >, or =.

1. $\frac{1}{4}$ ◯ $\frac{8}{11}$

2. $\frac{4}{9}$ ◯ $\frac{2}{11}$

3. $4\frac{6}{7}$ ◯ $4\frac{11}{20}$

Number of the Day ———————————————————

2

How many different two-dimensional figures can you find today?

_____

_____

_____

Facts Practice ————————————————————————

Multiply or divide.

1. 3×4 **2.** $12 \div 4$ **3.** 5×5

4. $25 \div 5$ **5.** 7×6 **6.** $42 \div 6$

Name _____ Date _____

Solid Figures

CA Standards
MG 3.6, MG 3.0

Name the solid figure that can be made with each net.

1.

_____

2.

_____

3.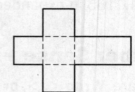

_____

Solid Figure	Number of Faces	Number of Edges	Number of Vertices
Rectangular Prism	4. _____	5. _____	6. _____
Square Pyramid	7. _____	8. _____	9. _____

✓ Test Practice

Circle the letter of the correct answer.

10. Nathan counted the faces on 3 different solid figures. He counted 15 total faces. If two of the solid figures were a cube and a triangular prism, what was the other solid figure?

   A triangular prism

   B square pyramid

   C triangular pyramid

   D rectangular prism

11. What solid figure has only 2 faces?

   A a cone

   B a cube

   C a sphere

   D a cylinder

Writing Math Name three different objects that are shaped like the following: cylinder, rectangular prism, and sphere.

Surface Area

Problem of the Day —————————————— MG 3.6

How many faces and how many vertices does a rectangular prism have?

Measurement and Geometry Review —————————— MG 3.5

Draw and label each.

1. acute angle *TUV*

2. obtuse angle *PQR*

3. right angle *DEF*

Word of the Day —————————————————— SDAP 1.2

median

The median of a roadway is something that runs down the middle of the road. What is the *median* of this set of data?

2, 2, 3, 5, 6, 6, 6, 8, 9

_____

_____

_____

Facts Practice ————————————————— KEY NS 1.9

Use a number line. Compare. Write <, >, or =.

1. $\frac{1}{2} \bigcirc \frac{6}{12}$

2. $\frac{3}{8} \bigcirc \frac{1}{4}$

3. $\frac{2}{3} \bigcirc \frac{7}{9}$

4. $\frac{5}{12} \bigcirc \frac{23}{60}$

5. $\frac{4}{7} \bigcirc \frac{16}{28}$

6. $\frac{9}{10} \bigcirc \frac{19}{20}$

Surface Area

CA Standards
MG 1.1, MG 1.4

Use the net to find the surface area of the solid figure.

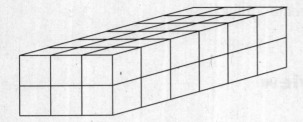   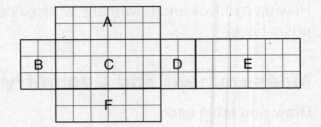

area of A = _____ square units   area of E = _____ square units

area of B = _____ square units   area of F = _____ square units

area of C = _____ square units   Total Surface Area = _____ square
                                         units
area of D = _____ square units

Find the surface area of each solid figure. Draw a net if you need to.

2. 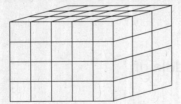   3.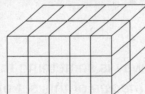

_____   _____

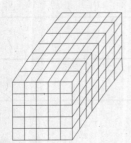

Writing Math Neal wants to know the surface area of this
rectangular prism. He has added 25 + 25 + 35 + 35 + 35 = 155
square units. What has he done wrong?

_____

_____

Volume

Problem of the Day ———————————————— MG 3.1

Tell whether the lines are intersecting, parallel, or perpendicular.

Number Sense ———————————————————— KEY

**Write the fractions in order from least to greatest.
Use the number lines on Workmat 4 to help you.**

1. $\frac{5}{5}, \frac{1}{5}, \frac{3}{5}$

2. $0, \frac{8}{10}, \frac{4}{10}$

3. $1, \frac{2}{8}, \frac{6}{8}$

Word of the Day ———————————————————— KEY

round

Round each number to the greatest place.

4,920

300,599

449,999

Facts Practice ———————————————————— NS 2.2

Estimate the product or quotient.

1. $123 \div 4$

2. $700 \div 8$

3. $815 \div 9$

4. 61×9

5. 68×84

6. 98×674

Name _____ Date _____

Volume

CA Standards
AF 1.4, MG 3.0

Find the volume of each figure.

1.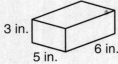
3 in.
5 in.
6 in.

2.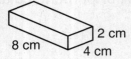
2 cm
8 cm
4 cm

3.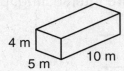
4 m
5 m
10 m

4.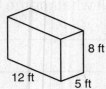
8 ft
12 ft
5 ft

_____

_____

_____

_____

5.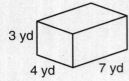
3 yd
4 yd
7 yd

6.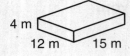
4 m
12 m
15 m

7.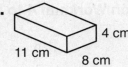
4 cm
11 cm
8 cm

8.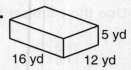
5 yd
16 yd
12 yd

_____

_____

_____

_____

Test Practice

9. A box is 8 cm long, 3 cm wide, and 1 cm high. What is the volume of the box?

   A 12 cm³

   B 24 cm³

   C 12 cm²

   D 24 cm²

10. The volume of a packing box is 24 cubic feet. The height is 2 feet, and the width is 4 feet. What is the length of the box?

    A 6 ft³

    B 18 ft

    C 3 ft

    D 192 ft²

Writing Math Sheila says that area is a measure of two dimensions, and volume is a measure of three dimensions. Do you agree? Why?

_____

_____

_____

_____

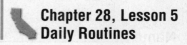
Problem Solving: Surface Area or Volume

Problem of the Day ———————————————————— MG 3.0

Victoria's father built a sandbox that is 11 feet long, 6 feet wide, and
has a height of 1 foot. How much sand will he need to fill the sandbox
to the top?

Measurement and Geometry Review ———————— MG 3.8

What are different ways you can describe a square?

Word of the Day ———————————————————————— MG 3.4

rotational symmetry

What is the only letter of the alphabet that has both line symmetry and
rotational symmetry?

_____

_____

_____

Facts Practice ———————————————————————— SDAP 2.2

Write the probability of each outcome as a fraction.

1. drawing a blue marble from a bag with 10 red and 6 blue marbles

2. rolling an even number on a standard number cube

3. landing on green with a spinner that has 3 yellow sections

4. tossing heads or tails with a coin

Name _____ Date _____

Problem Solving: Surface Area or Volume

Solve.

1. Jenni is wrapping a gift box that measures 4 ft × 5 ft × 2 ft. How much wrapping paper does she need?

   _____

2. Whitney is purchasing a box. She wants to know if she can fit a certain number of her books into the box. Should she calculate the volume or the surface area of the box?

   _____

   _____

3. Tony is buying siding to put on the outside of his house. In order to determine how much siding to buy, should he measure the volume or the surface area of his house? How do you know?

   _____

   _____

   _____

Test Practice

Circle the letter of the correct answer.

4. If the measurements of a box are 2 × 6 × 8, what is the volume of the box?

   A 16 units³   **B** 64 units³

   C 96 units³   **D** 152 units³

5. If the volume of a cube is 64 in³, What is the surface area of the cube?

   A 8   **C** 16

   B 64   **D** 96

 Writing Math Write a problem that uses surface area to solve.

_____

Looking Ahead Activities

Next year, you will learn more about
problem-solving with whole numbers
and fractions, geometry, and data.
The Looking Ahead activities will
help you get ready.

Name _____ Date _____

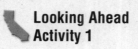
Number Mazes

CA Standards
NS 2.1 prepares for Gr. 5
KEY NS 2.1

By yourself

Draw a path through each maze so that your path goes only through expressions equal to the value given for the maze. Your path may include horizontal, vertical or diagonal moves. In each maze, several frames show the given value to help you find the path.

1. Value = 2.3

End

2.0 + 3.0	3.0 + 0.2	8.11 − 4.85	4.31 − 2.11	0.5 + 1.2	**2.3**
3.0 − 0.3	7.21 − 4.89	1.87 + 0.93	0.2 + 0.03	1.08 + 1.22	5.1 − 2.8
1.25 + 1.25	4.5 − 1.3	5.81 − 3.51	**2.3**	1.8 + 1.22	1.07 + 0.06
5.1 − 3.8	**2.3**	5.5 − 4.2	8.1 − 5.5	5.1 − 2.7	3.2 − 0.01
1.6 + 0.7	2.05 + 1.25	2.1 + 0.02	3.0 − 0.07	4.81 − 3.51	8.23 − 6.32

Start

2. Value = 5.14

End

1.8 + 3.14	4.82 + 1.32	4.28 + 0.68	3.31 + 2.13	9.05 − 4.37	**5.14**
4.5 − 1.33	6.5 − 0.91	6.5 − 2.36	9.87 − 4.53	5.14	7.2 − 2.06
6.1 − 0.86	3.37 + 1.57	7.32 − 1.87	7.2 − 2.6	0.94 + 4.2	6.22 − 4.1
5.1 + 0.4	8.23 − 2.99	**5.14**	7.13 − 3.99	8.13 − 2.99	0.14 + 4.1
2.49 + 2.65	6.05 − 0.91	0.42 + 9.4	3.47 + 1.67	2.94 + 2.56	6.2 − 2.06

Start

3. Value = 3.27

End

1.2 + 2.17	1.27 + 0.2	**3.27**	0.96 + 2.41	9.25 − 5.88	**3.27**
6.08 − 2.81	8.1 − 4.83	2.45 + 0.66	2.14 + 1.13	1.58 + 1.59	2.41 + 0.86
0.77 + 2.5	7.35 − 3.98	4.99 − 0.72	0.6 + 2.67	7.2 − 3.83	3.99 − 0.72
1.9 + 1.37	1.97 + 1.2	1.8 + 1.37	2.11 + 1.61	**3.27**	5.04 − 1.77
4.5 − 1.23	2.57 + 0.6	3.5 − 1.23	4.05 − 0.09	2.88 + 0.65	1.99 + 1.68

Start

Objective: Use addition and subtraction to solve problems involving decimals.

Equivalent Fractions

There are different ways to find equivalent fractions.

CA Standards
NS 1.5 and **KEY** NS 1.9 prepare
for Gr. 5 **KEY** NS 1.5

By yourself

Materials: fraction strips

You can use fraction strips.

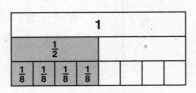

$\frac{1}{2}$ and $\frac{4}{8}$ are equivalent fractions.

You can use number lines.

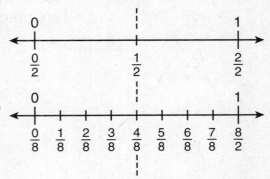

$\frac{1}{2}$ and $\frac{4}{8}$ are equivalent fractions.

**Decide whether the fractions are equivalent. Write *yes* or *no*.
Use fraction strips to help you.**

1. $\frac{8}{12}$ and $\frac{2}{3}$ 2. $\frac{3}{4}$ and $\frac{6}{8}$ 3. $\frac{5}{6}$ and $\frac{7}{10}$ 4. $\frac{1}{2}$ and $\frac{4}{6}$

_____   _____   _____   _____

5. $\frac{1}{4}$ and $\frac{3}{12}$ 6. $\frac{2}{3}$ and $\frac{4}{9}$ 7. $\frac{1}{3}$ and $\frac{3}{9}$ 8. $\frac{5}{6}$ and $\frac{10}{12}$

_____   _____   _____   _____

Find a fraction equivalent to each. Draw number lines to help you.

9. $\frac{2}{3}$ 10. $\frac{4}{12}$ 11. $\frac{2}{10}$ 12. $\frac{3}{4}$ 13. $\frac{1}{6}$

_____   _____   _____   _____   _____

14. $\frac{3}{3}$ 15. $\frac{2}{8}$ 16. $\frac{6}{9}$ 17. $\frac{3}{5}$ 18. $\frac{5}{10}$

_____   _____   _____   _____   _____

Objective: Use fraction strips and number lines to find equivalent fractions.

Name _____   Date _____

Factors

CA Standards
NS 4.0 prepares for Gr. 5
KEY NS 1.4

Here are two ways to find factors for 12 using a factor tree.

With your partner

One Way	Another Way
Write any pair of factors for 12.	Write a pair of factors for each factor until all of the factors are prime numbers.

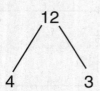

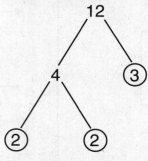

A prime number is a whole number that only has itself and 1 as factors.

$4 \times 3 = 12$, so 4 and 3 are factors of 12.

$2 \times 2 \times 3 = 12$, so the prime factors of 12 are 2, 2, and 3.

Make a factor tree for each number.

1. 16   **2.** 15   **3.** 24   **4.** 20

5. Make as many different factor trees as you can for 18.

Objective: Make and use a factor tree to find factors of a number, including prime factors.

Simplify Fractions

CA Standards
KEY NS 1.8 prepares for
Gr. 5 **KEY** NS 1.5

With your partner

A fraction is in simplest form when the only common factor of the numerator and denominator is 1.

You can simplify fractions using prime factorization.

Find the simplest form of $\frac{16}{20}$.

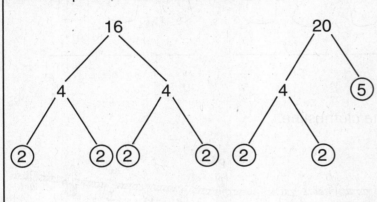

Step 1

Find the prime factors of each number.

Step 2

Find the factors that are the same and multiply.

$16 = \mathbf{2 \times 2 \times 2 \times 2}$
$20 = \mathbf{2 \times 2 \times 5}$

Think:
$\mathbf{2 \times 2 = 4}$

Then, divide the numerator and denominator by 4.

$\frac{16 \div 4}{20 \div 4} = \frac{4}{5}$

So, $\frac{4}{5}$ is the simplest form of $\frac{16}{20}$.

Write each fraction in its simplest form.

1. $\frac{8}{12}$ _____

2. $\frac{20}{24}$ _____

3. $\frac{6}{8}$ _____

4. $\frac{12}{24}$ _____

5. $\frac{6}{15}$ _____

6. $\frac{14}{20}$ _____

7. $\frac{12}{14}$ _____

8. $\frac{9}{24}$ _____

9. $\frac{12}{18}$ _____

10. $\frac{4}{8}$ _____

11. $\frac{9}{15}$ _____

12. $\frac{8}{20}$ _____

13. $\frac{12}{16}$ _____

14. $\frac{6}{12}$ _____

15. $\frac{14}{21}$ _____

16. $\frac{16}{24}$ _____

17. $\frac{8}{16}$ _____

18. $\frac{10}{15}$ _____

19. $\frac{20}{24}$ _____

20. $\frac{14}{20}$ _____

Objective: Use prime factorization to simplify fractions.

Fractions on a Number Line

CA Standards
KEY NS 1.9 prepares for
Gr. 5 **KEY** NS 1.5

By yourself

1. Write a fraction for each shirt on the clothesline.

___ ___ ___ ___   ___ ___ ___   ___ ___ ___

2. Write a fraction for each shirt on the clothesline.

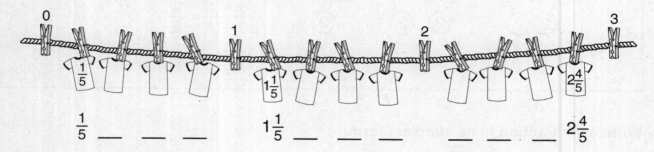

$\frac{1}{5}$ ___ ___ ___ $1\frac{1}{5}$ ___ ___ ___ $2\frac{4}{5}$

3. Write a fraction for each sock on the clothesline.

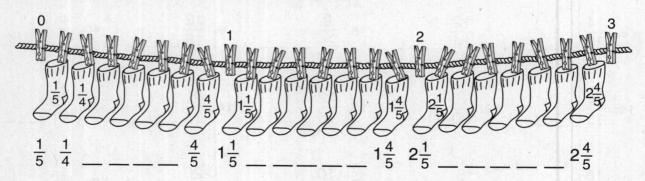

$\frac{1}{5}$ $\frac{1}{4}$ ___ ___ $\frac{4}{5}$ $1\frac{1}{5}$ ___ ___ $1\frac{4}{5}$ $2\frac{1}{5}$ ___ ___ $2\frac{4}{5}$

Objective: Name fractions on a number line.

Decimals on a Number Line

1. Write a decimal for each shirt on the clothesline.

0.1 ___ ___ ___ ___ ___ ___ ___ ___

2. Write a decimal for each shirt on the clothesline.

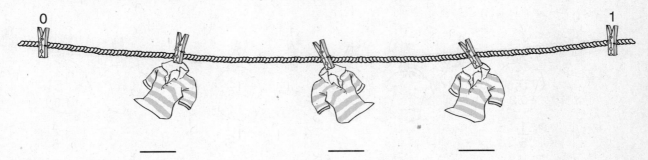

___   ___   ___

3. Write a decimal for each sock on the clothesline.

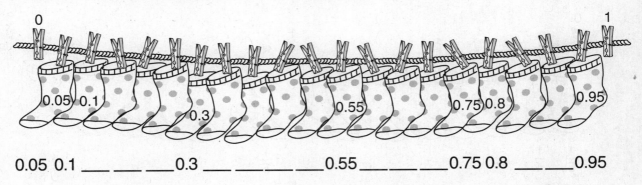

0.05 0.1 ___ ___ 0.3 ___ ___ 0.55 ___ ___ 0.75 0.8 ___ ___ 0.95

Objective: Name decimals on a number line.

Fractions and Decimals

CA Standards
KEY NS 1.9 prepares
for Gr. 5 **KEY** NS 1.5

By yourself

1. Write a fraction and decimal for each shirt on the clothesline.

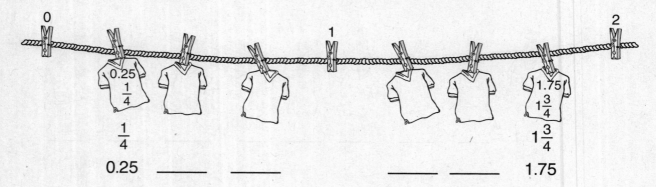

0.25 _____ _____ _____ _____ 1.75

2. Write a fraction and decimal for each shirt on the clothesline.

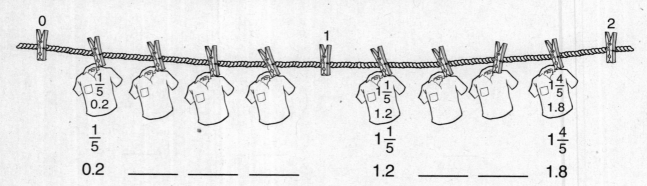

0.2 _____ _____ 1.2 _____ _____ 1.8

3. Write a fraction and decimal for each sock on the clothesline.

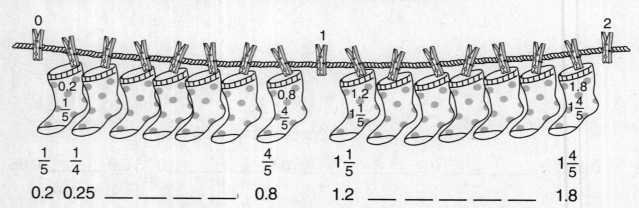

0.2 0.25 _____ _____ 0.8 1.2 _____ _____ 1.8

Objective: Name fractions and decimals on a number line.

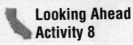

Round Numbers

CA Standards
KEY NS 1.3 prepares for
Gr. 5 NS 1.1

By yourself

Myra wants to round 3,642,864.
Write the letter that shows how Myra should round
the number to each place.

1. ____ ten thousands   **a.** 3,600,000

2. ____ thousands   **b.** 3,642,860

3. ____ tens   **c.** 3,643,000

4. ____ hundreds   **d.** 3,640,000

5. ____ hundred thousands   **e.** 3,642,900

Jason completed a crossword puzzle
for his math homework.
For each clue he had to round a number.
Write a clue for each answer. A sample is done for you.

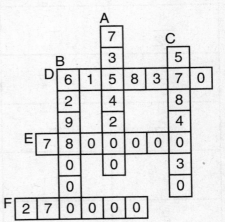

Down

A. Round 7,354,248 to the nearest hundred. _____

B. _____

C. _____

Across

D. _____

E. _____

F. _____

Objective: Round numbers through the millions.

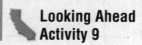
Add and Subtract Fractions

CA Standards
KEY NS 3.2 prepares for
Gr. 5 **KEY** NS 2.3

By yourself

Complete the table.
Write all sums in simplest form, including given sums.

1.	$\frac{1}{6}$	+	$\frac{3}{6}$	=	$\frac{4}{6}$ $\frac{2}{3}$
2.	$\frac{2}{10}$	+	$\frac{7}{10}$	=	
3.		+	$\frac{5}{9}$	=	$\frac{7}{9}$
4.	$\frac{1}{3}$	+	$\frac{2}{3}$	=	
5.		+	$\frac{2}{4}$	=	$\frac{3}{4}$
6.	$\frac{3}{12}$	+		=	$\frac{6}{12}$
7.	$\frac{4}{8}$	+	$\frac{2}{8}$	=	
8.	$\frac{5}{10}$	+		=	$\frac{6}{10}$
9.		+	$\frac{1}{8}$	=	$\frac{2}{8}$
10.	$\frac{2}{4}$	+		=	$\frac{3}{4}$
11.	$\frac{2}{5}$	+	$\frac{2}{5}$	=	
12.	$\frac{3}{8}$	+		=	$\frac{6}{8}$
13.	$\frac{5}{12}$	+	$\frac{2}{12}$	=	
14.		+	$\frac{3}{10}$	=	$\frac{5}{10}$
15.	$\frac{3}{8}$	+		=	

Objective: Add and subtract fractions with like denominators.

Division Practice

CA Standards
KEY NS 3.4 prepares for
Gr. 5 KEY NS 2.2

By yourself

Divide.

1. $5\overline{)86}$ 2. $2\overline{)53}$ 3. $4\overline{)507}$ 4. $6\overline{)735}$

5. $5\overline{)619}$ 6. $3\overline{)513}$ 7. $9\overline{)728}$ 8. $7\overline{)434}$

9. $94 \div 3$ 10. $76 \div 8$ 11. $231 \div 4$ 12. $802 \div 6$

_____   _____   _____   _____

13. $535 \div 2$ 14. $478 \div 3$ 15. $611 \div 7$ 16. $457 \div 9$

_____   _____   _____   _____

Solve each word problem.

17. Four children shared 97 pennies as equally as possible. How many pennies did each get?

_____

18. There are 8 rows of seats in a theater. Each row has the same number of seats. If there are 368 seats in the theater, how many seats are in each row?

_____

19. Vans need to be rented for a field trip. Each van can hold 9 children plus the driver. How many vans are needed for 140 children?

_____

20. Julia read a 154-page book in 2 days. She read the same number of pages each day. How many pages did she read each day?

_____

21. An artist had 255 glass beads. She used 7 beads for each bracelet she made. How many bracelets could the artist make using the glass beads?

_____

22. Mike has 460 baseball cards in his collection. He can fit 6 cards on each page of his card album. How many pages will Mike need for all of his baseball cards?

_____

Objective: Divide multidigit divisors by one-digit dividends.

10

Perimeter and Area

CA Standards
MG 1.1 and MG 1.4 prepare for
Gr. 5 **KEY** MG 1.1

By yourself

Anna's bedroom

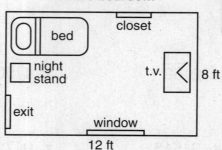

Anna's bedroom is 12 ft long
and 8 ft wide. She wants
to put a border around the room
and put new carpet on the floor.
How many feet of border does
she need? How many square
feet of carpet does she need?

To find how much border is needed, find the perimeter of the room.	To find how much carpet is needed, find the area of the room.
Perimeter = (2 × length) + (2 × width) $P = (2 × 12 \text{ ft}) + (2 × 8 \text{ ft})$ $P = 24 \text{ ft} + 16 \text{ ft}$ $P = 40 \text{ ft}$ So, Anna needs 40 ft of border.	Area = length × width $A = 12 \text{ ft} × 8 \text{ ft}$ $A = 96 \text{ ft}^2$ So, Anna needs 96 ft² of carpet.

Find the perimeter and area of each rectangle.

1.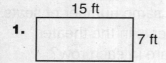

$P = $ _____

$A = $ _____

2.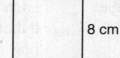

$P = $ _____

$A = $ _____

3.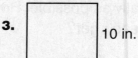

$P = $ _____

$A = $ _____

4.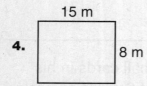

$P = $ _____

$A = $ _____

5.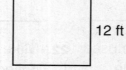

$P = $ _____

$A = $ _____

6.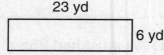

$P = $ _____

$A = $ _____

Objective: Use formulas to find the perimeters or areas of polygons.

Kite Angles

Kites come in many sizes and shapes. The drawing shows the plan for a large kite. Look at the different angles in the plan.

CA Standards
Mg 3.1 prepares for
Gr. 5 KEY MG 2.1

With your partner

Materials: ruler

When you draw an angle, you use 3 letters to name it. The middle letter always stands for the endpoint, or vertex, where the two rays meet.

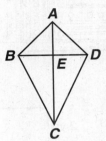

Use the kite plan to answer questions 1–3.

1. Angle *AEB* is a right angle. Name three other right angles found in the kite plan.

   _____

2. How can you classify angle *ABC*?

   _____

3. Use triangle *ADC* to complete the table. Name the three angles found in the triangle and then classify each angle as acute, obtuse, or right.

Angle Name	Type of Angle

Draw and name each angle.

4. acute angle

5. obtuse angle

Objective: Identify and draw right, acute, and obtuse angles.

Name _____ Date _____

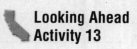
Area of Complex Figures

CA Standards
MG 1.4 prepares for
Gr. 5 **KEY** MG 1.1

By yourself

What is the area of
Mrs. Walter's garden?

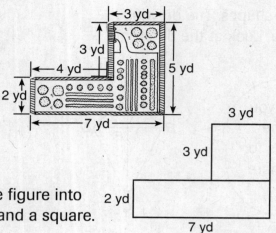

Step 1 Separate the figure into a rectangle and a square.

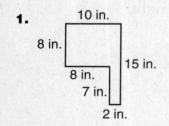

Step 2 Use a formula to find the area of each figure.

Area of the Rectangle
Area = $l \times w$
$A = 7$ yd $\times 2$ yd
$A = 14$ yd²

Area of the Square
Area = $s \times s$
$A = 3$ yd $\times 3$ yd
$A = 9$ yd²

Step 3 Add both areas to find the area of the whole figure. 14 yd² $+ 9$ yd² $= 23$ yd²
So the area of Mrs. Walter's garden is 23 yd².

Find the area of each figure.

1.

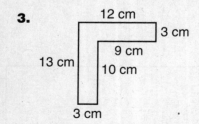

$A =$ _____

2.

9 m
2 m
5 m   4 m
3 m
5 m

$A =$ _____

3.

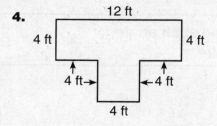

$A =$ _____

4.

12 ft
4 ft   4 ft
4 ft→   ←4 ft
4 ft

$A =$ _____

Objective: Find the area of complex figures.

Name _____   Date _____

Make Geometric Solids

The patterns below are called nets.
Copy each net onto one-inch grid paper.
Cut out the net and fold it on the dotted lines.
Name the solid figure each net makes.

CA Standards
MG 3.6 prepares for
Gr. 5 **KEY** MG 1.2

With your partner

Materials: one-inch grid paper, scissors, tape

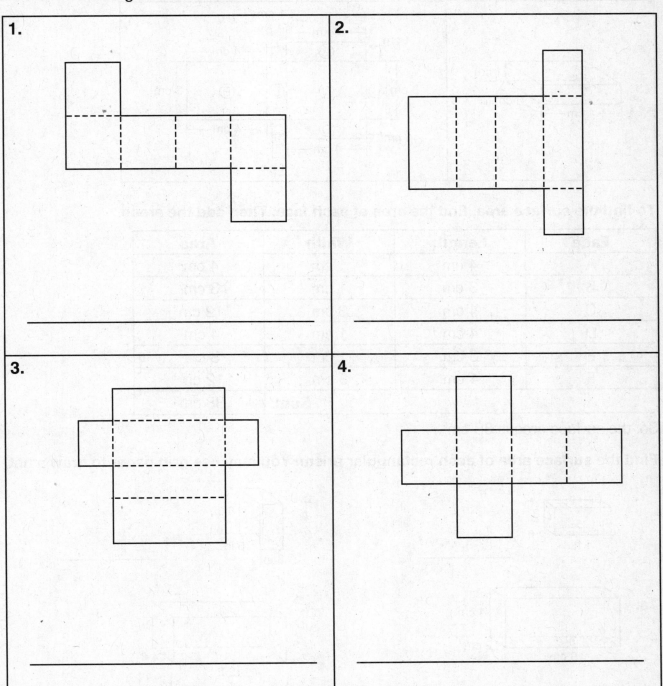

1.

_____

2.

_____

3.

4.

_____   _____

Objective: Use nets to make models of cubes and rectangles.

Surface Area of Rectangular Prisms

CA Standards
MG 1.2 and MG 1.3 prepare for
Gr. 5 **KEY** MG 1.1

With your partner

Materials: grid paper

The surface area of a solid figure is the sum of the areas of all its faces. You can use a net to show all of the faces.

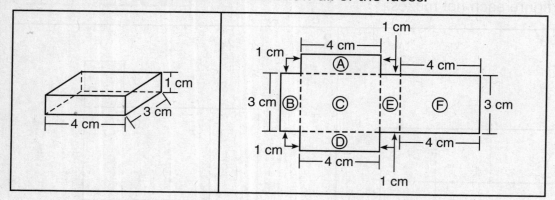

To find the surface area, find the area of each face. Then add the areas.

Face	Length	Width	Area
A	4 cm	1 cm	4 cm²
B	3 cm	1 cm	3 cm²
C	4 cm	3 cm	12 cm²
D	4 cm	1 cm	4 cm²
E	3 cm	1 cm	3 cm²
F	4 cm	3 cm	12 cm²
		Sum:	38 cm²

So, the surface area is 38 cm².

Find the surface area of each rectangular prism. You may use grid paper to draw a net.

1.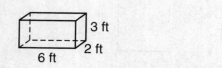
3 ft
2 ft
6 ft
_____

2.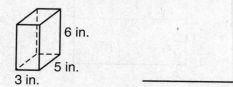
6 in.
5 in.
3 in.
_____

3.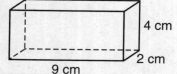
4 cm
2 cm
9 cm
_____

4.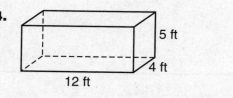
5 ft
4 ft
12 ft
_____

Objective: Find the surface area of rectangular prisms.

What's My Rule?

CA Standards
AF 1.1 prepares for
Gr. 5 KEY AF 1.5

With your partner

Write the rule for each table.

1.

Set A (input)	Set B (output)
3	9
7	13
4	10
8	14
11	17
5	11

2.

Set A (input)	Set B (output)
0	0
5	20
2	8
8	32
1	4
7	28

3.

Set A (input)	Set B (output)
9	6
15	12
6	3
25	22
13	10
3	0

_____   _____   _____

Take turns playing "What's My Rule?" with a partner.
Think of a rule for the first table and fill in the first 4 rows.
Your partner names the rule and completes the table.

Set A (input)	Set B (output)

Set A (input)	Set B (output)

Set A (input)	Set B (output)

Set A (input)	Set B (output)

Set A (input)	Set B (output)

Set A (input)	Set B (output)

Objective: Describe the relationship between two sets of related data.

Patterns in Tables of Numbers

CA Standards
AF 1.1 prepares for
Gr. 5 KEY AF 1.5

With your partner

For each input-output table below:

• Study the rows that are complete to find the rule for the table.

• Write the rule below each table.

• Choose numbers from the box to complete the table according to the rule. Numbers in the box can be used more than once or they are not used in any table.

| 3 | 8 | 12 | 20 | 36 | 5 | 13 | 19 | 21 | 29 | 31 | 27 | 45 |

1.

Set A (input)	Set B (output)
	6
	4
22	11
6	
4	2
16	8
24	12

_____

2.

Set A (input)	Set B (output)
1	6
15	
13	18
17	22
22	
7	
0	

_____

3.

Set A (input)	Set B (output)
11	33
9	
4	12
7	
12	
8	24
15	45

_____

4.

Set A (input)	Set B (output)
15	7
21	
28	
9	1
	4
32	24
8	0

_____

5.

Set A (input)	Set B (output)
6	
14	
29	36
42	49
56	63
31	38
38	

_____

6.

Set A (input)	Set B (output)
4	
7	35
9	
10	50
	25
0	0
1	5

_____

Objective: Describe the relationship between two sets of related data.

Name _____   Date _____

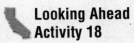
Find My Rectangle

CA Standards
SDAP 1.1 prepares for
Gr. 5 KEY SDAP 1.5

With your partner

Materials: grid paper

In this activity, you will use a coordinate grid to play a game with a partner. Each of you takes turns for the roles of artist and guesser.

1. The artist draws a rectangle in a coordinate grid and labels the endpoints of the rectangle *A, B, C,* and *D.*

2. The artist also writes next to each letter the coordinates of each point.

3. The artist then tells the guesser the lengths of the sides of the rectangle.

4. The guesser records the lengths of the sides of the rectangle on the top of a separate sheet of graph paper.

5. The guesser's task is then to figure out the exact location of the rectangle. To to this, he or she names points, one at a time.

   • When a guesser names a point inside the rectangle, the artist must say "Inside."

   • When a guesser names a point outside the rectangle, the artist must say "Outside."

   • When a guesser names a vertex of the rectangle, the artist must indicate *A, B, C,* or *D.*

   • When a guesser names a point on a side of the rectangle, the artist must say "On the side."

6. Play continues until the guesser can draw the rectangle. Players then exchange roles.

Objective: Locate and name points on a coordinate grid.

Make a Line Plot

CA Standards
SDAP 1.0 prepares for
Gr. 5 SDAP 1.2

With your group

1. Rory took a survey and collected his data in a tally table.
Make a line plot to represent Rory's data.

Number of Cousins	
Cousins	Tally
0	I
1	III
2	
3	IIII
4	II
5	⩩ I
6	⩩
7	IIII
8	⩩ II

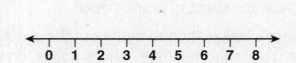

2. Work with your group to take your own survey.
Record your data on the tally table.
Make a line plot of your data.

Objective: Make a line plot to represent data.

Mode and Median

Trevor conducted a survey of 15 baseball players. He asked them how many home runs they hit this season. His data are shown in the line plot. What is the mode and median of the data?

CA Standards
SDAP 1.2 prepares for
Gr. 5 SDAP 1.1

By yourself

The mode of the data is the number that occurs most often. The number of home runs that occurred most often was 1.
The mode is 1.

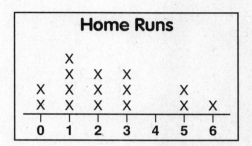

Home Runs

The **median** is the middle number when a set of numbers is arranged in order from least to greatest.

0 0 1 1 1 1 2 **2** 2 3 3 3 5 5 6

The median, or middle, of the data set is 2.

Write the median and mode for the data in each line plot.

1.

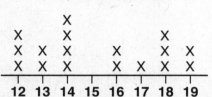

Weight of Dogs

mode: _____ median _____

2.

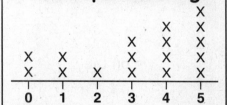

Hours Spent Reading

mode: _____ median _____

3.

Number of Pets

mode: _____ median _____

4.

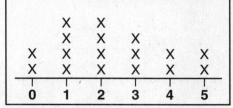

Baskets Made

mode: _____ median _____

Objective: Identify the mode and median of a data set.